P9-CDJ-069

BACHELOR BROTHERS'
—BEDSIDE—
COMPANION

Bachelor Brothers' Bedside Companion

Bill Richardson

Illustrated by Rose Cowles

Douglas & McIntyre
Vancouver / Toronto

96 97 98 99 00 5 4 3 2 1

Douglas & McIntyre Ltd.
1615 Venables Street
Vancouver, British Columbia V5L 2H1

Canadian Cataloguing in Publication Data
Richardson, Bill, 1955-
Bachelor Brothers' bedside companion

ISBN 1-55054-517-5

I. Title
PS8585.I186B335 1996 C813'.54 C96-910410-3
PR9199.3.R467B335 1996

Editing by Saeko Usukawa
Design, illustrations and typesetting by Rose Cowles
Printed and bound in Canada by Friesens
Printed on acid-free paper

The publisher gratefully acknowledges the assistance of the Canada Council and of the British Columbia Ministry of Tourism, Small Business and Culture.

Acknowledgements

Some of the pieces in this book were published, in different form, in the *Vancouver Sun*, the *Georgia Straight* and the *Globe and Mail.* For permission to reprint copyright material, the author and publisher gratefully acknowledge the following: Diane Ackerman, from *The Moon by Whale Light*, copyright © 1991 by Diane Ackerman, reprinted by permission of Random House Inc.; Margaret Atwood, "Variation on the word sleep" from *Selected Poems 1966-84*, copyright © 1990 by Margaret Atwood, reprinted by permission of Oxford University Press Canada; Weldon Kees, "The End of the Library" from *The Collected Poems of Weldon Kees*, edited by Donald Justice, copyright © 1975 by the University of Nebraska Press, reprinted by permission of the University of Nebraska Press; Rose Macaulay, from *Personal Pleasures*, copyright © 1990 by The Estate of Rose Macaulay, first published in 1990 by The Ecco Press, reprinted by permission; Gwendolyn MacEwen, "The Vacuum Cleaner Dream" from *Armies of the Moon,* copyright ©1972 by Gwendolyn MacEwen, reprinted by permission of The Estate of Gwendolyn MacEwen; Adrienne Rich, "Aunt Jennifer's Tigers" from *Collected Early Poems 1950-1970*, copyright © 1993, 1951 by Adrienne Rich, reprinted by permission of the author and W. W. Norton & Company Inc.; Carol Shields, from *Swann*, copyright © 1987 by Carol Shields, reprinted by permission of Random House of Canada Ltd.; Wallace Stevens, "Disillusionment of Ten O'Clock" from *Collected Poems*, copyright © 1923 and renewed 1951 by Wallace Stevens, reprinted by permission of Alfred A. Knopf Inc.; John Updike, "Tossing and Turning" from *Collected Poems 1953-1993*, copyright © 1993 by John Updike, reprinted by permission of Alfred A. Knopf Inc.

To Saeko Usukawa
midwife to bachelors

Contents

Prelude

Off the coast, there is a strait. In the strait, there is an island. On the island, there is a valley. In the valley there is a house. And in the house live two brothers, Hector and Virgil. They are fraternal twins and the co-proprietors of the Bachelor Brothers' Bed & Breakfast. It is a retreat. An escape. A sanctuary of sorts. It is a place where people go to whittle down the pile of books they've always meant to read but for which they've never made time. It is not for everyone. There are none of the recreational amenities one might find at a posh resort or on a cruise. There are no theme dances, no parlour games or skit nights, although a bracing game of croquet is available to those who crave exertion of an aerobic nature. There is always a Scrabble board open and waiting on the library table.

Over the years, the brothers have developed the habit of setting down in a book their observations of the day by day goings-on in their inn and community. Here, they keep a record of their own reading and attach or copy out informational bonbons that strike them in the moment as entertaining or useful or both. The result is this bedside companion, a gumbo of poems, formulae, letters from guests, trivia, receipts, lists, sundries and notions, charms and incantations: textual relaxant that can be taken in small doses by a reader looking for a minute or two of diversion before surrendering to Morpheus. The words are meant to amuse and distract. Now and then they might provoke a thought or two, but never so serious a speculation that it can't be set to one side and dealt with in the morning.

The brothers' good and talented friend Rose Cowles provided the illustrations, and they know very well how much they owe to her. They would also like to acknowledge the contributions of Altona Winkler, astrologer, cosmetician and romance consultant, and of their handyman and hagiographer, Caedmon Harkness. To all our friends, wherever you make your beds, and however you lie in them, we wish you the sweetest repose, as well as swift and sure deliverance from ghoulies and ghosties and long-legged beasties and things that go bump in the night.

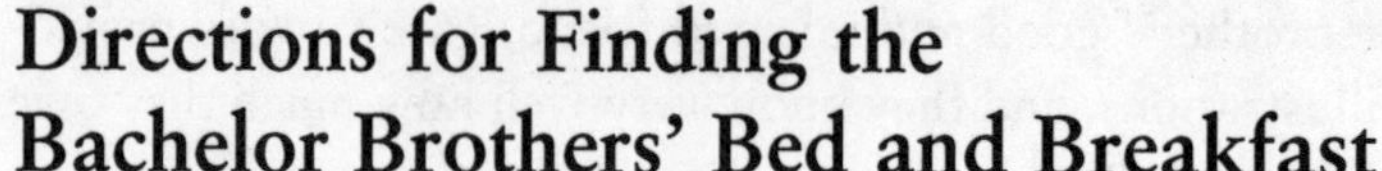

Directions for Finding the Bachelor Brothers' Bed and Breakfast

No, no,
there are no maps.
The best way to guarantee arrival—
if guarantees are among your requirements—
is to achieve, however you can,
that state of understanding whereby
cartography's utility ends with the fact
that maps spelled backward gives you Spam.
When that much is clear to you,
you are already halfway there.
Pardon me?
Oh, I see.
You're still trying to weigh the anchor
of specificity.

All right, then. Try this.
Take the road that leads in all directions
and follow every fork.
Go slow in the valleys.
Asphalt will give way to gravel
as the road and your journey
begin to unravel.
If the season is right, there will be lambs
in the field with the lightning-blasted tree.
You might smell honeysuckle,
but this means nothing. Don't be deceived.
Listen for bagpipes and listen for bees.
Notice when time starts to slow and thicken,
wait for your heart and pulse to quicken.
There is a sign. It is clearly marked.
A blind man couldn't miss it in the dark.
Remember—use caution when steering by stars.
Turn back, turn back, if you get to the sea.
It means you have gone too far.

Virgil: A Few Words

This past Christmas, my twin brother Hector presented me with a hot water bottle. This has been his dependable Yuletide remembrance each and every year since we were four. It was then, as it would be now, an *outré* gift for one preschool brother to give another. But the peculiarity of his choice was mitigated by the fact that it was not something he set out to purchase deliberately with me in mind. The first of these many hot water bottles was something he happened to spy on a cluttered white elephant table at a church rummage sale. He had never seen such a contraption before and mistook it—understandably—for a hardy strain of balloon. That was what he believed he had purchased, and that was what he told me it was when I stripped it of its tissue paper swaddling and held it aloft 'twixt thumb and forefinger, as though it were a fish.

There is a photograph of me in an old family album, my cheeks distended and my eyes dilated, a baby step away from falling victim to infantile apoplexy, huffing and puffing into the resistant rubber. Mother, who believed that experience was the best teacher, let me wheeze into it for fully half a frustrating hour before disabusing us of our misunderstanding. When she uncorked the floppy flask and went to fill it, she unwittingly released a genie who possessed me, thoroughly and forever. I will never forget how I held that thermal miracle to my chest; how I was flooded with a deep and abiding sense of peace. The hot water bottle eclipsed every other gift I received that year. Firetrucks, paint-by-number sets, a bow and arrow, a model sailboat: none of them

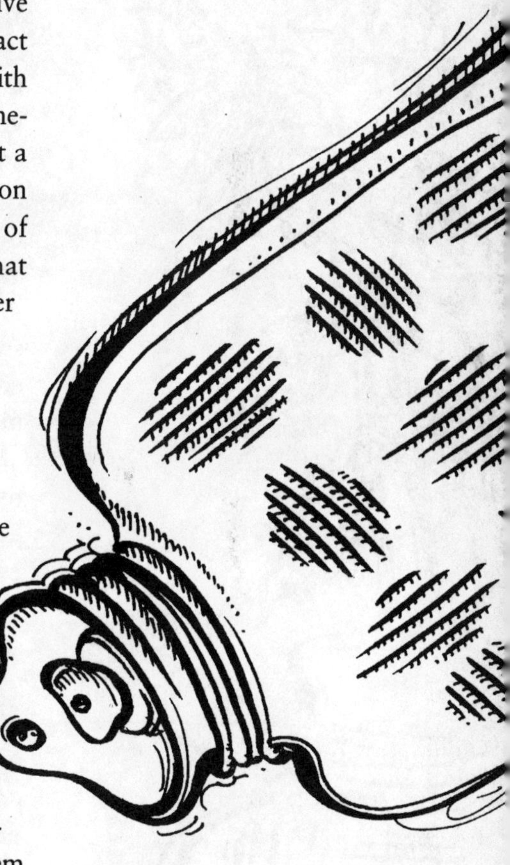

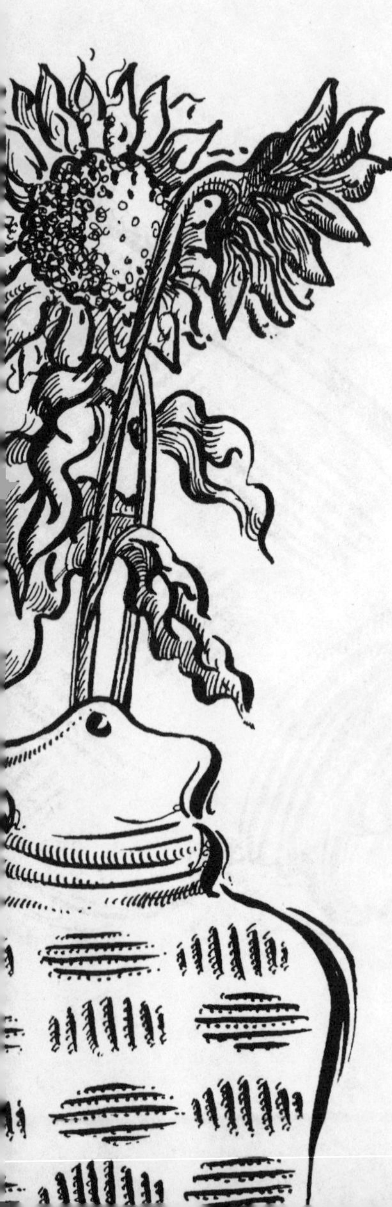

could hold a candle to this little bag of warmth. I wandered around the house all day clutching it. That night, I clasped it to my loins, close and tight. It was a singularly erotic moment. What happiness was mine, all those many years ago, when I was merely four! Hector was so pleased with my reaction to his haphazard present that he made it a point to purchase one for me the next year, and the year following, and thus was a tradition forged.

Fleet-footed time, where have you gone? Were I a sentimentalist who needed to preserve every fragment of his passing life, I would by this point have more than fifty of the things in my charge and keeping. However, my relationship with these comforting bladders could be best described as "serially monogamous." I am faithful to one the livelong year, and then cast it aside in favour of the new arrival. This is not as grim or as callous as it sounds. No one could ever accuse me of overburdening some landfill. Oh, no! I am nothing if not environmentally minded. The ecological imperative of reduce, reuse, recycle is one of my most trusted mantras, and it's been twenty years since I actually consigned a hot water bottle to the trash. I keep two in a bottom drawer, as a safeguard against the dreadful possibility of leakage in the current model. And I always have a few on the miscellaneous shelf of our linen closet, should one of our visitors be stricken with a flu, or a depression, or cramps, or one of the other ennuis that only a hot water bottle can assuage.

For the others I find creative uses, and believe me, they are good goads to lateral thinking. Covered with a doily or a gaily crocheted overcoat, they make effective hot plates. Dabbed with *papier-mâché*—in order to correct the flaccidity to which they are naturally heir—and painted up to a fare-thee-well, a hot water bottle can be used to good effect as a bud vase. Babies of my

acquaintance have discovered that they are useful teething tools. Retrievers find them every bit as satisfying as a tennis ball to fetch, and their owners—especially those who are given to myopia—claim they are much easier to find in the underbrush. Add a quarter cup of plaster and some water, shake and leave to dry, and you have a doorstop without peer. I have had occasion to use a hot water bottle as a martini shaker, and have seeded a couple with navy beans to make durable maracas for the rhythm band in the seniors' home across the valley. Last spring, during a prolonged bout of very rainy weather, our hired hand, Caedmon Harkness, availed himself of one of these disused, dusty vessels. With a few snips of the garden shears and the clever addition of some leather thonging, he made himself a pair of E-Z wash sandals to wear while tromping about our lawns and garden. As with so much else in this life, a hot water bottle's possibilities are limited only by our imaginative reach and grasp.

For as long as I can remember, these thoughtful Christmas remembrances from my brother have always been the same, have never been subject to anything like stylistic variation. Without fail, he will purchase the standard-issue regulation rubber model, liverish of hue and capped with a silvery metal stopper; the kind that is readily available for well under twenty dollars from Abel Wackaugh's Hardware and Hair Styling Emporium, just half a mile down the road.

I take great pleasure in such consistency. I should be disappointed, I think, if some morning, while the old familiar carols bleated from the radio, I were to rip the colourful paper from the predictable, pliable package that waits for me beneath the tree to discover that it concealed something in plaid, or royal blue, or platinum. Something in rainbow stripes with a thermostat or dig-

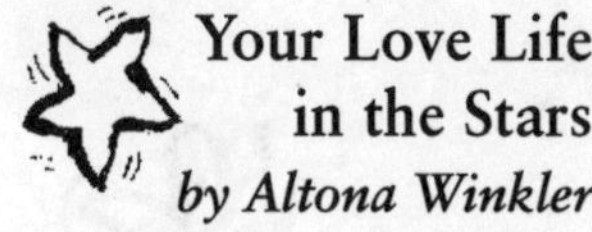

Your Love Life in the Stars

by Altona Winkler

CAPRICORN

December 22 to January 19

Be patient with your mate, Capricorn. Remember that in the grand scheme of things, it really doesn't matter a jot or a tittle if he or she leaves clothes in a heap in a corner of the room night after night, or is chronically late, or if his or her outlandish braying embarrasses you at parties. Of course, you would be well advised to remember that in the grand scheme of things it also doesn't matter if you dump him or her immediately and link up with someone younger, sexier, and smarter. Hey! You're a grownup! Make up your own mind!

ital thermometer or remote control. Something with a designer label. Oh, no! That would be unthinkable. I know what I like. And what I like is the unadorned. Simplicity unalloyed.

"Oh, Virgil. You are such an old woman at times!" Mother would say, with what I like to believe was affection, when I would tiptoe past her bedroom *en route* to my own with my steamy nighttime companion clutched to my bosom and a murder mystery—the more sordid the better—under my arm. She would give her head a "where did I go wrong?" shake and go back to fitting a ship into a bottle, or applying a decal to the wing of a model fighter plane, or pinning a chloroformed butterfly to a board.

Lepidopterology was one of her passions. When we were very young, she would take us with her on butterfly-hunting expeditions around the valley. I remember how we would sit in the shade and read aloud to one another from Omar Khayyam, looking up from time to time to see her bounding over copse and field, her net in one hand and her specimen jar in the other, intent on capturing some fluttering, waxy-winged prey. She was a remarkable sight, six feet tall, swathed in coveralls and a cardigan, sporting her father's old fedora. She looked rather like a scarecrow who had been sprinkled with fairy dust and had come lurching to ungainly but purposeful life.

Poor Mother! There can be no doubt that we were a disappointment to her. A lusty indiscretion on a hot afternoon had landed her with twin bastards. She was bitter, and I can't say I blame her. We took over first her body and then her life. She was never able to set aside the notion that the least we could have done, by way of recompense, was to have shared her interests and avocations, which were of a practical and

scientific bent. Alas, we would have had to unravel the DNA to which we fell heir and knit it into an altogether reconfigured helix for such a wish to be made flesh. It was antithetical to our natures to stay up all night with her in the hope of glimpsing a passing comet, or to spend hours in her workshop learning how to use a lathe or a bandsaw. Auto mechanics were beyond us, and we could neither of us tell a piston from a fan belt from a femur.

It was a good thing she had her parrot, Mrs. Rochester, to serve her as soul mate. Mrs. Rochester—who lives with us still, and who, I am convinced, serves as a conduit for the voice of Mother from the great beyond—was only too happy to sit beside her mistress's workbench and offer suggestions as to which tool would best serve which purpose.

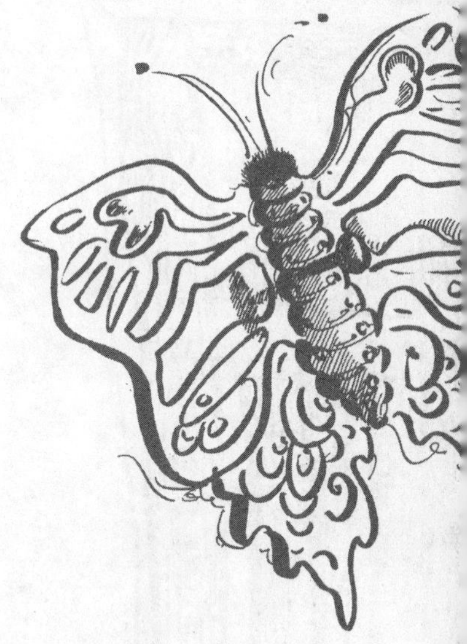

"Crescent wrench," she would sputter, while littering the floor with sunflower seed husks. "Rasp file."

"Isn't it ironic," I once remarked to Mother as we were heading home after an afternoon of butterfly chasing, "that mother contains the word moth?" I was keenly aware of her disappointment in us and was grasping at ingratiating straws.

"Ironic? *Mo*ronic is more like it," she snarled. And pulling her fedora low over her brow, she charged ahead, her knapsack clinking with mortuary jars, the wind whistling through her deadly net, her sweater flapping, and Mrs. Rochester on her shoulder singing the "Toreador Song" from *Carmen.*

I won't pretend I wasn't hurt by such sniping. I was. But the wounds she inflicted were superficial and quick to heal. Neither Hector nor I sustained any permanent damage from Mother's offhand and sometimes cutting dismissals. This is what I believe, although some would point to our long-held bachelor status, our apparent lack of willingness to have wives, as proof that such glib assurances are hollow. Although I see the psychoanalytic logic operative in such thinking, I don't credit it. We, her sons, understood early on that it was not in her nature to nurture. But nor was she an ogre. Hector and I both knew that our mother loved us, in her fashion. That night, for instance, she made up for her abruptness by teaching us the words to one of her favourite rugby songs. And when I went to bed, I found a green and blue butterfly pinned to my door. It was the best she could do. I loved her. I will always miss her. And I blame her for nothing, as there is no blame to lay. It is not because of who she was or what she said and did that we live as bachelors.

We have quite different ideas, Hector and I, as to the art of bachelorhood. Hector cast aside the principle of celibacy directly after Altona Winkler moved to the neighbourhood, and they became what I believe is called "an item." That romance has been going on for years now. I can only suppose that their interpelvic play is lively, as Hector often returns from their assignations looking as if he has been to a tractor pull. And before he goes off to Altona's house for a conjugal visit, I can hear him in the bathroom, slapping on aftershave lotion and growling at himself in the mirror.

As for me, however, when the book of my life has been written, and the index has been compiled, anyone looking up the word "intercourse" will find only passages describing my conversational interaction with friends and guests. Am I an anomaly in a carnally obsessed world? Perhaps I am. Certainly, my heart goes out to the angels who are stuck each night with standing by the posts of my bed, who keep vigil over Virgil. How they must envy their lambent colleagues who were lucky enough to snag clients with nocturnal habits that are entertaining. I imagine them, these agents of the benign and divine, scudding over the clouds, their wings an ivory blur, all in a rush to clock in with the agency from which they receive their evening's assignment. In Heaven, as it is on earth, it's first come, first served. The quickest of the cherubs to reach the dispatcher are given the jobs where passion and intrigue run high in bedrooms made lively by the amorous cries of young lovers. Who would be more fun to keep from harm? A couple of sexual athletes who pause every so often to refer to the *Kama Sutra*? Or a parched old bachelor with a cup of cocoa at his side, a cat on his head and a hot water bottle clenched between his legs? A grizzled codger who moves his lips while plodding his way through a book called *How To Read German*, which was left behind years ago by a scholarly guest. And who is that bachelor, you ask? Oh, why should I be coy? I am he. He is I. We are one.

How To Read German languished on our shelves for the longest time. I don't think I would ever have troubled to look into it had it not been for the recent nocturnal escapade of one of our visitors, who is both a retired general and an energetic somnambulist. While the rest of the house dreamed, he rose from his bed—still sleeping himself, though wholly ambulatory. He came down to the library, where he proceeded to disencumber a whole range of shelves of their books and arrange them into a fortress. We found him in the morning, marching up and down in front of

his creation, standing guard, holding a copy of *How To Read German.* Luckily, his wife appeared before we tried to wake him, which tactic she told us might have been dangerous. She simply barked out, "Soldier! Present arms!" Then she relieved him of the text, handed it to me, took him by the elbow and marched him back to his room. He appeared for breakfast an hour later, looking chagrined but otherwise perfectly refreshed.

∞

All things work out for the best in the end. Those bookcases were sorely in need of dusting. And I, idly flipping through that road map to the Teutonic tongue, found a trove of intelligence I can scarcely believe I've lived without. Every night, I drink some of it in.

"Die Tibeter sind ein glückliches Volk mit einem kindlichen Humor," I mutter, inhaling the dander from Waffle's tail. It dangles over my upper lip, a Kaiser moustache. I give in to the urge to sneeze.

"Gesundheit," Mrs. Rochester cackles kindly, peering down at me from the lintel above the door.

"Danke," I answer, flipping through a German-English dictionary. With its help, I make tonight's phrase out to be "The Tibetans are a happy people with a childlike sense of humour." By gum, that's a good one. One can never tell when such a sentiment might come in handy in a place like this: a bed and breakfast in which we, the hosts, must always have a conversational starter on hand in case the flow of chat bogs down around the breakfast table. What could be more laxative in such a situation than to look about brightly and beam, "I say! Did you know that the Tibetans are a happy people with a childlike sense of humour?"

A Short Cut for Nonlinguists is the subtitle of the book from which I culled so fascinating a morsel. From this same text, which

In his autobiography, The Story of My Life, *Augustus Hare tells the story of a woman who "awoke in the night with the disagreeable sense of not being alone in the room, and soon felt a thud upon her bed. There was no doubt that someone was moving to and fro in the room, and that hands were constantly moving over her bed. She was so dreadfully frightened that she at last fainted. When she came to herself, it was broad daylight, and she found that the butler had walked in his sleep and had laid the table for fourteen upon her."*

is meant to make the language of Goethe and Schiller accessible to engineers and software salesmen, I have learned about how bees communicate through dancing, about how dairy operations have been changed by mechanized milking, and that the state of Jodhpur in India absorbs solar energy which equals the present energy consumption of the whole world. I once owned a pair of jodhpurs and found them unbearably hot. Now I know why.

Somewhere I read—and I can't think of why I didn't set it down, as it's exactly the sort of information I like to file away for future use—that the body risks losing some remarkable percentage of its heat during sleep, and that its major points of egress are the head and the feet. I defend myself against the latter danger by wearing thick woollen bed socks. I deal with the former peril by encouraging Waffle to sleep on my thinning pate. It took a while to train her to this. I actually anointed my skull with a tincture of catnip, which resulted in some painful scratches until we both settled into the arrangement. And, of course, I have my new hot water bottle to clutch to my middle, just for good measure. Socks, cat and bottle. All are in place. It is time to say *guten Abend* to *How To Read German* and all its fascinating insights. Tomorrow night, I will read about the mating rituals of the crane (*die Kraniche*). Outside, the ruffian storms of January are stomping their boots and gunning their engines. They'll never find me here, though.

Close your eyes and feel how the air around you is full of the quiet electricity of all the world's dreaming, praying, wishing. Close your eyes and settle into your own body's weight and rumbling. Close your eyes. Repeat after me. Surrender, surrender, surrender. Sweet dreams, always.

From *The Gul's Horne-booke*
by Thomas Dekker

For do but consider what an excellent thing sleep is. It is so inestimable a jewel that if a Tyrant would give his crown for an hour's slumber it cannot be bought. Of so beautiful a shape is it that though a man lie with an Empress his heart cannot be at quiet till he leaves her embracements to be at rest with the other. Yea, so greatly indebted are we to this kinsman of death that we owe the better tributary, half our life, to him; and there is good cause why we should do so, for sleep is that golden chain that ties health and our bodies together. Who complains of want, of wounds, or cares, of great men's oppressions, of captivity, whilst he sleepeth? Beggars in their beds take as much pleasure as kings. Can we therefore surfeit on this delicate ambrosia?

Tossing and Turning
by John Updike

The spirit has infinite facets, but the body
confiningly few sides.
                                        There is the left,
the right, the back, the belly, and tempting
in-betweens, northeasts and northwests,
that tip the heart and pinch circulation
in one or another arm.
                                        Yet we turn each time
with fresh hope, believing that sleep
will visit us here, descending like an angel
down the angle our flesh's sextant sets,
tilted toward that unreachable star
hung in the night between our eyebrows, whence
dreams and good luck flow.
                                        Uncross
your ankles. Unclench your philosophy.
This bed was invented by others; know we go
to sleep less to rest than to participate
in the orthic twists of another world.
This churning is our journey.
                                        It ends,
can only end, around a corner
we do not know
                    we are turning.

Hector: Some Words to Help You Sleep

Insomnia is not a frequent visitor to my bed. In fact, I am one of the few who is never stopped and interrogated at the border of the Land of Nod. They let me pass in without question, and I only run into trouble when they try to make me return home again. But on those rare nights when slumber passes me by, I know of no sleep-inducing opiate more effective than simple counting. It is surely no accident that the first four letters of the word "number" spell what they spell. There is something so lulling, so anaesthetizing about the dull recitation of digits, that I wonder how mathematicians can evade somnolence at work.

Everyone to whom I've spoken about this has a different method. Some begin at one and work up. Some count only the odd numbers, others the even. Still others prefer to count backward from a thousand, or to direct their attention to the left chest and take a census of the heartbeats. And then there are those who really and truly do count sheep. I've never understood why sheep had this responsibility foisted on them, rather than cows or rabbits. Perhaps it's because "sheep" is but a consonant removed from "sleep." Here is an ancient rhyme that was used by working shepherds—in the field, so to speak—to keep track of wandering sheep. It is a good formula to keep in reserve for those nights when the more mundane methods of numbering the flock just don't seem to be having the desired effect.

Yahn, Tayn, Tether, Mether, Mumph,
Hither, Lither, Auver, Dauver, Dic,
Yahndic, Tayndic, Tetherdic, Metherdic, Mumphit,

Yahn a mumphit, Tayn a mumphit,
Tethera mumphit, Methera mumphit,
Jig it.

You might want to append to this a counting-out rhyme from Mother Goose.

Anery, manery, dipry, dick,
Delia, dollia, dominick,
High cha, pigh cha, dominicha,
High, low, dock.

Finally, here is a passage from Osbert Sitwell's account of his travels in China, *Escape with Me!* These are the names of some of the 131 varieties of chrysanthemum that a retired Manchu civil servant was able to identify in 1900. The trick with this lovely list is to memorize it and to repeat it slowly to yourself, all the while visualizing an impossibly colourful and lavishly scented garden.

"Honey-linked Bracelets, Silver-Red Needle, Peach-Blossom Fan, Eyebrows of the Old Ruler, Concubine of the Hsiao and Hsiang Rivers, Goose Quills, Purple Tiger Whiskers, Ash Crane Wings, Spring Swallow in an Apricot Orchard, Snow-covered Cinnabar, White Crane Sleeping in Snow, Azure Lotus, Jade Shoots, Egg Plant Blue; and Golden-Hair Lion, Golden Phoenix Wing, Purple Dragon with Open Claws, Egret Crane Feathers, Azure Dragon-Whiskers, Lustrous Variegated Cloud-Dragon, Jade Spoon Stirring Broth, Autumn Beauty of the Hibiscus, Evening Sun on a Duck's Back, Lily on a Dazzling Day; and Black Tiger-Whiskers, Golden Phoenix Holding a Pearl in its Mouth, Spring Dawn at

the Han Palace, Red Mist, Half Water Half Sky, Bird's Talon Immortal, Intoxicated T'ai Po, Phoenix Flute, Fragrant White Pear, Gold as One Likes It, Yellow Orioles in the Green Willow, Beehive Quartz as One Likes It or Unicorn and Parrot . . ."

If all these counting methods fail, I recommend keeping a copy of Aquinas by the bed. I have never known anyone to remain awake after five minutes with Aquinas after 8 P.M.

Out in the Dark
by Edward Thomas

Out in the dark over the snow
The fallow fawns invisible go
With the fallow doe;
And the winds blow
Fast as the stars are slow.
Stealthily the dark haunts round
And, when the lamp goes, without sound
At a swifter bound
Than the swiftest hound,
Arrives, and all else is drowned;
And I and star and wind and deer,
Are in the dark together—near,
Yet far,—and fear
Drums on my ear
In that sage company drear.

How weak and little is the light,
All the universe of sight,
Love and delight,
Before the might,
If you love it not, of night.

Reading What the Wind Brought: New Year's Resolutions

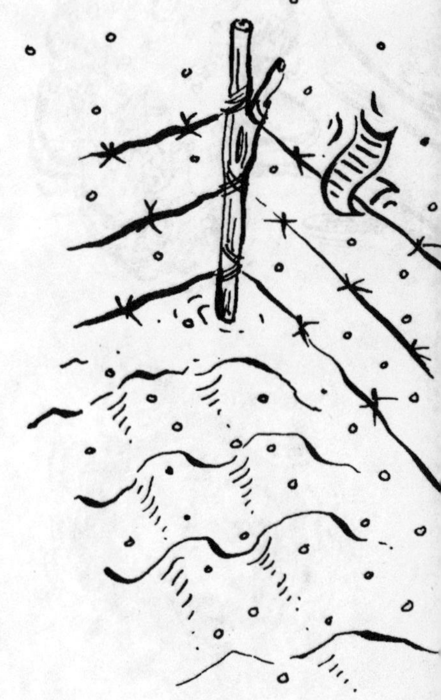

One of the joys and liabilities of living on this island is that deer are thick on the ground. To look up from some mundane task like washing the dishes just in time to see a doe and her fawn step from the woods and into the yard brings you about as close to God as you'd care to be, this side of Heaven. But, oh dear, the deer! The way they strip the trees of their bark. The devastation they wreak on a garden that already has a rough row to hoe simply because we two brown-thumbs are its caretakers! This is enough to make you reach for *The Joy of Cooking* to check out the prescribed venison treatments.

Prophylactic measures need to be taken to safeguard the plant life. We surround the trees with a protective circle of chickenwire, and we have fenced off the garden with barbed wire. It is unsightly but effective. What's more, it has a utility that goes beyond forestalling the deer from dining on tender shoots. The thorny barbs are adept at snagging odd bits of the world as they blow through this part of the valley. Shopping lists, advertising brochures, ferry schedules, bus transfers, personal memos, lip-

stick-stained napkins from far-away cocktail lounges: all manner of ephemera travels this way on the wind. It's good to get such unlooked-for news. It assures us that the outside world winds on.

Just the other day, we found the following optimistic verse on the wires. Significantly, not one of the resolutions catalogued below was accompanied by a check mark. We imagine the writer fed it to the wind before embarking on his or her course of self-improvement. This strikes us as an eminently sensible thing to have done.

Be It Resolved, from One to Fifty

(1) Drink more water, (2) swear off wine,
(3) Swear off swearing, (4) cease to whine.
(5) Eat more broccoli, (6) cut out cheese,
(Au revoir to runny Bries).
(7) Cigarettes, we tell you *Ciao!*
(8) Coffee, take your final bow!
(9) Meet all deadlines with a smile,
(10) Rise at six to run ten miles,
(11) Snack on fruit between your meals,
(12) Read more Proust, less Danielle Steel.
(13) Yoga class will keep you spry,
(14) Do your stretches, (15) join the Y.
(16) Be unfailingly polite
When, at 6 o'clock each night,
Just as you are primed to eat
(17) (beans and tofu—nix on meat)
Someone phones with wares to sell:

Do not tell them "Go to hell."
(18) Smile at babies when they howl,
(19) Chuckle when they void their bowels
At the table next to yours.
(20) Gladly do your household chores,
(21) Shun despair and (22) cleave to hope,
(23) Do not make fun of the Pope.
(24) Keep in touch with far-flung friends,
(25) Do not borrow, (26) gladly lend.
(27) Cut your power bill by half,
(28) Leave off snorting when you laugh,
(29) Do not gossip—seal your lips,
(30) Do not open perfumed strips
When you browse through magazines,
(31) Try to live within your means.
(32) Tell the truth, yet (33) be discreet,
(34) Do not lose your tax receipts,
(35) Give more freely to the poor,
(36) Thank-you notes are *de rigueur.*
(37) Stay at home, (38) don't gather moss,
(39) Brush your teeth, (40) and always floss,
(41) Purge all dust from ledge and shelf,
(42) Love thy neighbour as thyself.
(43) Stress requires a ready vent,
(44) Keep abreast of world events.
(45) Keep the dryer free of lint,
(46) Freshen up your breath with mint,
(47) Keep the tub and toilet scoured,
(48) Don't sing Verdi in the shower.
(49) Do not waste your precious time,
(50) Start this morning. End this rhyme!

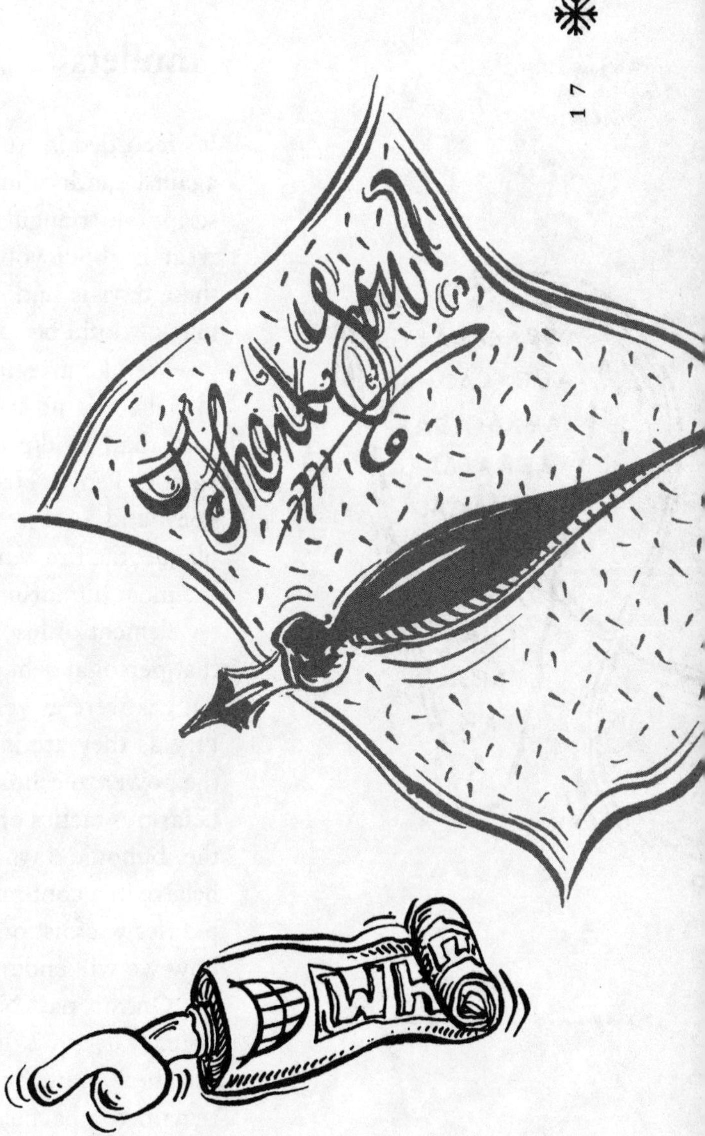

Amulets to Write and Wear

It's recorded in Aubrey that if you want to safeguard your person against sundry illnesses and agues, you should copy out this prescription, triangularly as shown, onto a piece of parchment and wear it about your neck. Writing it down is a cinch. The trick these days is finding parchment. But then, no one ever promised magic would be easy.

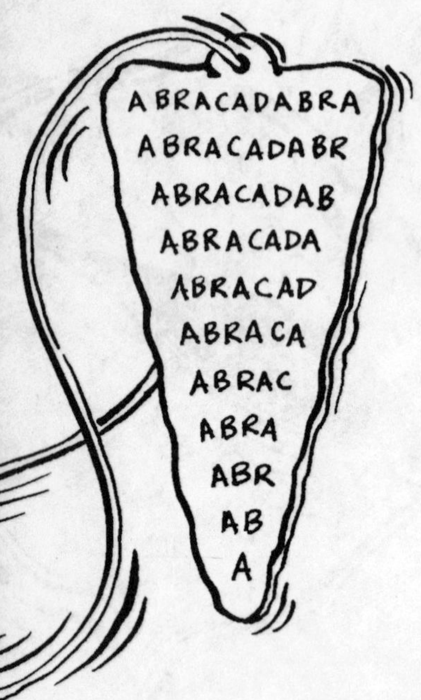

We like a regular dose of Aubrey. And to our way of thinking, there is no better way to measure the stately march of the year than to dip each day into the diary of his contemporary, Samuel Pepys. His diurnal accounts of life in London between 1660 and 1669 set events of looming historical significance (the plague, the fire, various military engagements) cheek by jowl with the most humdrum of domestic concerns. Curiously, it is the latter element of his record that we find most compelling. To know that personal debt and little vanities, domestic discord and intestinal gas were as vexing and preoccupying in the seventeenth century as they are in our own, and that they had, in the moment, the power to eclipse in the mind of the writer his fretting over the nefarious tactics of the Dutch navy or the growing death toll from the bubonic invasion is somehow encouraging. It makes us believe in a continuum; it makes us believe that in spite of the stupidities we foist on ourselves, on others and on the planet, somehow we will endure.

On this past New Year's Day, we read Pepys's diary entry for January 1, 1662. It made us suppose that his long-suffering wife, Elizabeth, must have wished now and then that her husband had remained a bachelor. It begins: "Waking this morning out of my

sleep on a sudden, I did with my elbow hit my wife a great blow over her face and nose, which waked her up with pain—at which I was sorry. And to sleep again."

Could it be that the poor woman had neglected to wear her Abracadabra amulet to bed? Herein lies a lesson for us all. Another amulet, much in favour in medieval times, is an amalgam of five Latin words arranged so that they can be read up and down, backward and forward. *Sator* is the sower. *Arepo*, the plough. *Tenet*, words. *Opera*, works. And *Rotas*, wheels. Copy this out and keep it beneath your pillow, and pleasant dreams will be yours.

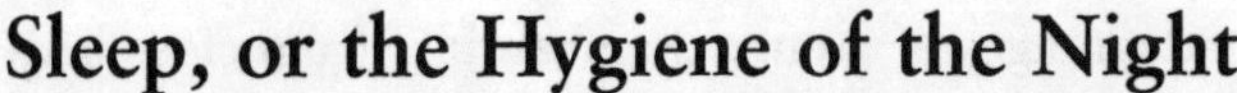

Sleep, or the Hygiene of the Night

Here are some cheering words by the Canadian physician Dr. W. W. Hall, from his 1870 tract *Sleep, or the Hygiene of the Night*:

All know that emanations are constantly passing from the body, its impurities, its dead and effete matter, which nature has no use for, and which she is constantly endeavoring to cast off by the pores of the skin, the average number of which for each square inch of the body is estimated by Erasmus Wilson to be two thousand five hundred, or seven million in all, making, if joined together, a canal twenty-eight miles long, which conducts from the system every twenty-four hours, in a state of sensible perspiration, or water called "sweat," or insensible perspiration, called "vapor," three pounds and a half from one person in the ordinary occupations of life, and much more in extraordinary callings. For example, men employed in keeping up the fires in the gasworks were found to have lost in weight, on an average, over three pounds in forty-five minutes, while some, in an unusually hot place, lost as much as five pounds two ounces in seventy minutes' work.

The insensible perspiration from a sleeper during the night is of itself enough to taint the atmosphere of a whole room, even a large one, as almost every reader has noticed on entering a sleeping-chamber in the morning after having come directly from the out-door air; and it is the breathing and rebreathing of an atmosphere contaminated in the variety of ways alluded to, which makes the night the time of attack of the great majority of violent human ailments; it is this which fires the train of impending disease, and which would have been deferred, if not entirely warded off, with the advantages of a pure chamber. It is from close bedrooms come the racking pains of fever, its torturing thirst, and speedy death; this it is which wakes up the cholera morbus, the cramp colic, the bilious diarrhea, and the multitudes of other ailments which surprise us in the night-time, and from which it is worthy of repetition, a night of good sleep in a clean, pure, and well-ventilated chamber would have effected a happy deliverance, as expressed in the familiar phrase of "sleeping it off."

Advice from Enquire Within Upon Everything *for Those Who Lie in the Beds They Make*

Beech-tree leaves are recommended for filling the beds of poor persons. They should be gathered on a dry day in the autumn and perfectly dried. It is said that they smell grateful, and will not harbour vermin. They are also very springy.

Feather beds should be opened every third year, the ticking well dusted, soaped and waxed, the feathers dressed and returned.

Recipe for Obtaining Good Servants

Enquire Within Upon Everything is a Victorian compendium of household hints and outright commandments, and a great source of formulae and recipes. If ever we need to know how to clean kid gloves or how to remove water spots from black crepe, we can turn with confidence to *Enquire Within*. Our hired hand Caedmon Harkness was recently perusing its pages and called our attention to these recommendations for dealing with servants:

There are frequent complaints that, in these days, servants are bad, and apprentices are bad, and dependents and aiding hands generally are bad. It may be so. But if it is so, what is the inference? . . . *How influence will descend!* Conscientiousness is spread, not only by precept but by example, and, so to speak, by contagion, it is spread more widely. Kindness is communicated in the same way. Virtue of every kind acts like an electric shock. Those in contact with its practitioners receive the communication of it. The same with qualities and tempers that do no honour to our nature. If servants come to you bad, you may at least improve them; possibly almost change their nature. Here follows, then a recipe to that effect:—*Recipe for obtaining good servants.*—Let them observe in your conduct to others just the qualities and virtues that you would desire they should possess and practise as respects you. Be uniformly kind and gentle. If you reprove, do so with reason and with temper. Be respectable, and you will be respected by them. Be kind, and you will meet kindness from them. Consider their interests, and they will consider yours. A friend in a servant is no contemptible thing. Be to every servant a friend; and heartless, indeed, will be the servant who does not warm in love to you.

They that wash on Monday,
Have all week to dry;
They that wash on Tuesday,
Are not so much awry;
They that wash on Wednesday,
Are not so much to blame;
They that wash on Thursday,
Wash for shame;
They that wash on Friday,
Wash in need;
And they that wash on Saturday,
They are sluts indeed.

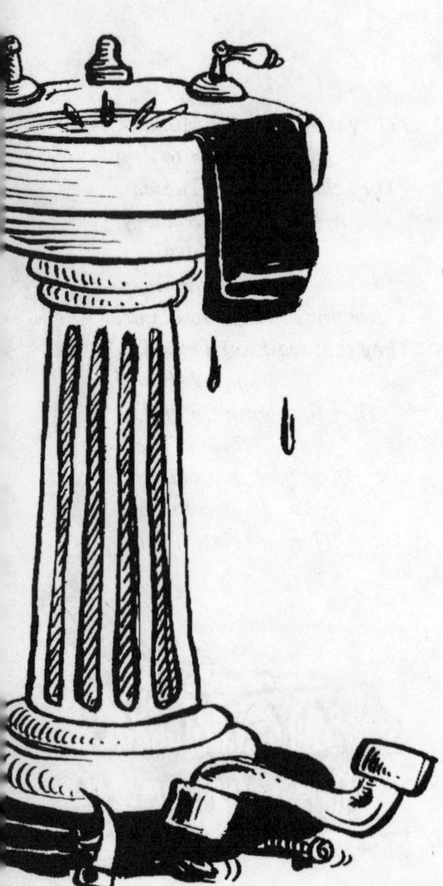

Caedmon Harkness: Hired Hand and Hagiographer

It was almost three years ago, after a great deal of to-ing and fro-ing, that I finally settled into a comfortable vocational niche. I came to work as the hired hand, the contented and general dogsbody, at the Bachelor Brothers' Bed & Breakfast. This was never what I imagined or foresaw for myself when I was going through my "what do I want to be when I grow up" phase, a stage of life that lasted until I was well into my forties. Nevertheless, it suits me. I am happy here. I derive huge satisfaction from the puttering and tinkering, the cooking and cleaning, the rudimentary tasks of maintenance and upkeep that fill my days. There is no dearth of chores or challenges to keep me occupied. This is an old and eccentric house. It creaks. It sags. Small fissures are forever appearing in ceilings and walls. Doors swell, tiles lift, faucets and pipes drip. Something is always threatening to give way. Sometimes, there is a wholesale letting go. There is no end to my "to do" list.

Busy though I am, I never feel pressured to keep up a frantic pace. My employers have a *laissez-faire* attitude towards the more niggling and petty particulars of housekeeping. No one could ever call them obsessed with detail or overburdened with perfectionism. As long as there are no dustballs rampaging around the kitchen; as long as water runs when the taps are turned; and as long as there are no direct threats to life or limb from some emerging domestic idiosyncrasy or aberrance, they are quite content to let things be. They allow me to be self-assigning about my projects, and I have ample time to develop my other interests.

Chief among these is hagiography. I have been fascinated by the lives and legends of holy men and women since I was a little boy. Indeed, my last failed business venture before finding shelter at the bed and breakfast was a mail-order enterprise called "The Saint of the Month Club." I thought it was a dynamite, no-fail idea. A stroke of brilliance! Subscribers—had there been any—would have received a hand-crafted bread-dough medal bearing a likeness of the chosen saint whose feast day falls in that month, along with a short biography of the anchorite and a prayer of my own devising. Alas, there were no takers. Why it failed so dramatically is still a mystery to me. I can only suppose it had something to do with the fact that we live in a relentlessly secular age. Then too, it might have been a function of marketing.

I may have made a strategic error in launching the concept in February. Perhaps I underestimated the rooted hegemony of St. Valentine's Day. I simply imagined that most of the rest of the population was, like me, sick to death of lacy cards and saccharine verses all done up in the name of a third-century Roman martyr who had nothing whatsoever to do with love. So it was that I offered my initial subscribers a "Valentine's Day Alternative Package." They could choose from among four saints other than Valentine, all of whom have February feast days. After all, is there any good reason why one should not remind one's beloved of one's undying affection on February 2, St. Brigid's Day?

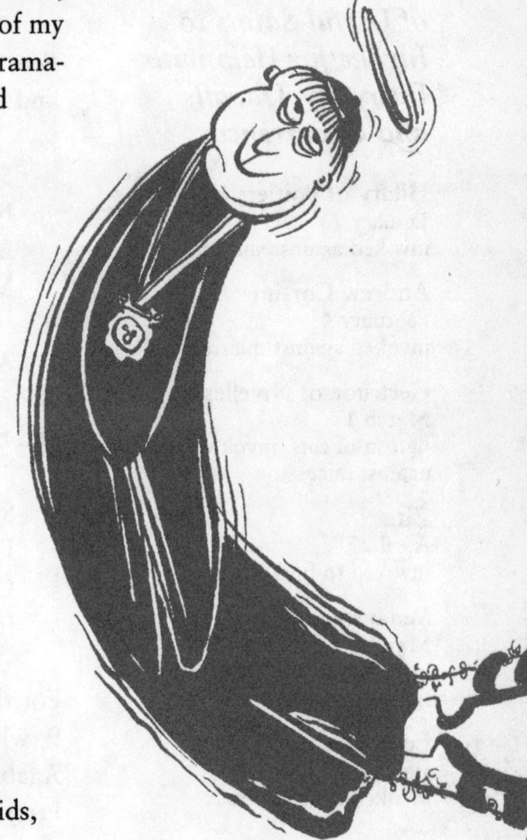

St. Brigid, who has a complex portfolio, is the patron saint of (among many others) poultry raisers, dairy maids,

fugitives and nuns. What heart would not leap like a hart at receiving a fond inscription along these lines?

Honey, you're terrific, and I only want to say
Won't you be my Brigid on this next St. Brigid's day?
You've milked me for devotion, and you've got a lot of pluck!
Steal my holy heart away, you great big handsome buck!

Why, I think that would be grand! And let's not overlook February 5, St. Agatha's Day. Agatha is the patron of bell makers and wet nurses, and is invoked against volcanoes. Hence:

Sweetheart, when you're gone from me, my life's a living hell.
None but you, my honeybunch, can ring my private bell.
Be my darling Agatha! I'm ready to explode!
My breast is overflowing with this loving overload!

And who wouldn't care to be remembered on February 19, St. Conrad's Day? Conrad is the saint invoked against both famine and hernia.

Sugarplum, I know you well, and now I will divulge
I love your hairy midriff with its herniated bulge.
Oh say that you won't tuck it in, won't let the surgeon carve.
If you'll not be my Conrad, then I'll just lie down and starve!

For the final selection, I considered the possibilities of February 9, which is St. Apollonia's Day (invoked against toothache); St. Agabus's Day on February 13 (patron of fortune tellers); and St. Peter Damian's Day on February 21 (invoked against headache).

Caedmon's List of Useful Saints to Invoke for Help with Everyday Travails and Occurrences

Hilary of Poitiers
January 13
invoked against snakebite

Andrew Corsini
February 4
invoked against quarrels

Gertrude of Nivelles
March 17
patron of cats, invoked against mice

Zita
April 27
invoked to find lost keys

Venantius
May 18
invoked against danger of falling

Leufredus
June 21
invoked against flies

I finally settled on St. Walburga's Day, observed on the 25th. Walburga is invoked against frenzy. My verse, which was very much to the point, went:

Sweetie on the 25th please be my own Walburga
Get me in a frenzy and we'll have a private merger.

Alas, none of it was to be. Consumers greeted my introductory offer with a resonant silence that consigned the whole project to the scrap heap. Ah, well. I still produce my monthly medals and prayers for my own amusement. And I take consolation in the certainty that I was just years ahead of my time. And timing, as anyone who has ever tried to co-ordinate a soft-boiled egg with the emergence of a slice of wholewheat toast will tell you, is everything. At eggs and toast, at least, I am an unqualified success, every time. And now, that time is up.

Goar
July 6
invoked against whirlpools

Albert of Trapani
August 7
invoked against demonic possession

Fiacre
September 1
invoked against hemorrhoids

Gomer
October 11
patron of unhappy husbands, invoked against hernia

Gregory the Wonderworker
November 17
invoked against earthquakes and floods

Valerian
December 15
invoked against the cold

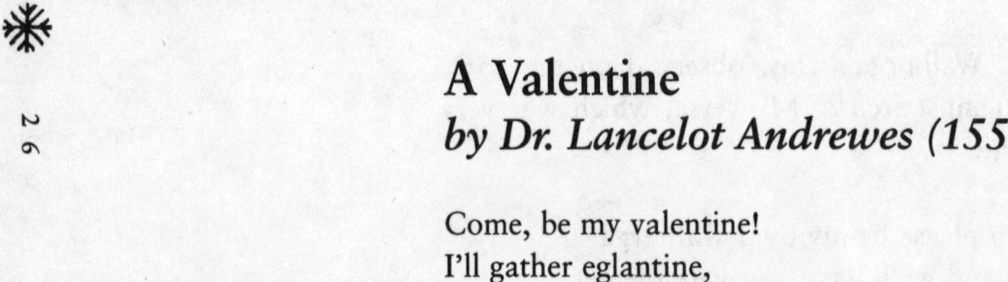

A Valentine
by Dr. Lancelot Andrewes (1555-1626)

Come, be my valentine!
I'll gather eglantine,
Cowslips and sops-in-wine,
With fragrant roses;
Down by thy Phillis sit,
She will white lilies get
And daffodillies fit
To make thee posies.
I bear in sign of love
A sparrow in my glove,
And in my breast a dove—
This shall be all thine.
Besides of sheep a flock,
Which yieldeth many a lock,
And this shall be thy stock,—
Come be my valentine.

Our Guests Write: B.

Dear Boys:

I'm going to have to cancel that reservation I made for next month. Life seems to have thrown out yet another of its intricate snares, and I've been caught, big time. I know this is the third time I've pulled the plug, and you must think I'm the King of the Chowder Heads. But really, when your best friend asks you to be one of her bridesmaids, what can you say but yes? Yes, you say, without thinking, forsaking all blindfolds and damning the torpedoes months in advance of their firing. Yes is what I said when my best friend asked, and I'm very glad I did. Even if the date that she and her spouse-to-be settled on coincides with my projected descent on the BBB&B.

"We'll have to find some title for you," she said, "other than bridesmaid, I mean. How about 'bridesmate'?"

"Fine," I said, still reeling with the unexpected honour of it all. "Bridesmate will be just fine."

"Great. Now, all the men in the wedding party will have kilts, so I thought you might want one as well."

"Kilt?"

"We'll rent them. Anita will be my other bridesmaid, and she'll be wearing blue. I'll have the dressmaker do you up a vest in matching material, so you might want to take that into account when you pick your tartan."

"Sure!"

When your best friend asks you to be a bridesmate at her wedding and suggests you wear a kilt that goes well with blue, what can you say but sure?

"And remember to leave some room in your sporran."

"Room? Sporran?"

A look of impatience skated over her otherwise radiant countenance. I could tell she wished she'd chosen a bridesmate who was less vague.

"You have to leave room in your sporran because you'll need to carry the ring. And my lipstick."

"I suppose I should bring along some Kleenex," I added, getting into the sporran-stuffing spirit of the event, "just in case we all break down." I was going to suggest I might squeeze in a few sandwiches, too; but as I couldn't attest to the elasticity of my unseen rent-a-sporran, I decided not to raise false hopes.

So there you have it. The wedding is a month away, and I am a bundle of nerves at the prospect of making my debut in this supporting but pivotal role. Bridesmate! I feel an overwhelming need to do some research. But where? This is not a well-established position in the highly regulated world of weddings and not much discussed in the extensive literature on nuptials etiquette. I'm going into this thing with a great many questions unanswered. For instance: Should I book an hour in a tanning salon so as not to embarrass the bride with my legs, which are the colour of library paste? Who wore the kilt before me, and how was he girded beneath the folds of tartan? Was it properly dry cleaned? Am I obliged to ask the best man to dance? Will I be able to cram everything in my sporran? And what if said sporran jams at some crucial moment, when a ring, a lipstick, a Kleenex, a sandwich, a wrench, or a volume of Martha Stewart is most required? What if some hitherto unknown virus comes to roost and engenders "sporran lock," a condition no one in the hall will be able to diagnose or repair? What then, my friends? What then? Such is the twisted path my thinking runs as the day draws nigh and tension builds.

The bride and groom, I'm pleased to say, are jitter free. They aren't tense in the slightest way. They've organized a celebration that will chug along ticketyboo, like a well-oiled machine. They've calmly and deliberately taken every bull by the horns, checked off every item on their respective "to do" lists, never seemed distraught, overwrought or unsettled. They've been unfailingly loving, caring, supportive and good-humoured towards their families, friends and each other.

Weddings are emotion-filled occasions and should make us cautious about using superlatives. But I can say truly, truly, that I have never seen two happier people, or two people who are more deserving of that happiness. I love them both. It will be a privilege to be with them and to stand up for my best friend as her bridesmate. As long as I stay standing, that is. If I faint dead away, I hope someone thinks to check the sporran. Somewhere, next to the lipstick and the flashlight, there'll be smelling salts.

Yours,

B.

A Cautionary Note on Pigging
by Dr. James Graham

Dr. James Graham, an eighteenth-century London physician, had this to say in a lecture against double beds:

There is not, in my opinion, anything in nature which is more immediately calculated totally to subvert health, strength, love, esteem, and indeed everything that is desirable in the married state, than that odious, most indelicate, and most hateful custom of man and woman continually *pigging* together, in one and the same bed. Nothing is more unwise—nothing more indecent—nothing more unnatural, than for a man and woman to sleep, and snore, and steam, and do every thing else that's indelicate together, three hundred and sixty-five times—every year.

Reading What the Wind Brought: Pages from a Memoir

Here are some confessional musings that hooked themselves onto our fence. We suspect they may be pages from a memoir and hope the writer kept a carbon copy. It would be a shame for this breathless account to be omitted from some future autobiography.

Once, when I was in my early twenties and more in touch with my groinal chakra than I am now, I prepared for the arrival of my *paramour du jour* by whipping up a big vat of cream. My swain, who was older than I and more experienced in many regards (having grown up in Toronto and all) and who had earned the right to be skeptical of such baroque initiatives in the boudoir, nonetheless allowed me to dab the stuff here and there and patiently counted the ceiling tiles while undergoing the lingual ministrations that followed so calcium-rich and high-cal an anointing.

My ego has always run roughshod over my id, and even in those days when the hormonal tide knew no ebb, when it only flowed and flowed, I somehow couldn't shake the notion that all this was, at root, ridiculous. Not even stiff tsunamis of randiness could rearrange reality, and reality in this case was leagues removed from torrid anticipation. Expansive contact with hot human flesh—hot, for it was August—made the cream turn rancid more quickly than I would have thought possible. The sour smell of something like baby sick filled the room, an essence not recommended by aromatherapists for its pheromonal qualities. C., all festooned with goo, bore an alarming resemblance to a

papier-mâché project gone awry, or to one of those lava-caked citizens of Pompeii. And when I had a badly timed out-of-body experience and surveyed the scene from above, I saw that I looked like nothing so much as a mother cat cleaning her newborn kitten.

How risible! But then, one of the perils of being human is that we can't allow our animal functions to stand unadorned. Rather, we have to dress them up and turn them into Art. Were this not the case, would we have the toilet, the bidet, the convection oven, the blender, the birthing suite, the palliative care ward? To say nothing of the half pint of whipping cream and all the many other playthings we pack in our old kitbags when we go merrily into rut.

Just because I point out such things in no way means that I hold them in disdain. Oh, no! While it is true that time in its passing has dulled the edge of my erstwhile lustiness; while it is true that I have latterly undergone a paradigm shift that has left me believing harnesses are for horses, candles are for power outages and handcuffs are for criminals; while it is true that in a word association test the prompt "lubrication" would provoke the response "mechanic," I am the first to acknowledge that a kiss is still a kiss and a sigh is still a sigh and the fundamental things apply. What is also true, however, is that the carnal obsessions of yore now have to share custody of my sensibilities with an eroticism that has a decidedly more pedestrian, domestic focus. For now, in middle age, pleasure oozes up from deep and unanticipated wells.

For instance—and you knew there would be a for instance—last night I whipped some cream. This is no longer a frequent indulgence of mine, but I had made a chocolate chiffon pie and needed the stiff white peaks to finish the thing off. I used the elec-

Your Love Life in the Stars
by Altona Winkler

AQUARIUS
January 20 to February 18

You have two big decisions to make before Valentine's Day. I would advise something sleek, black and low cut. And French food is always nice. But it would be smart to make a reservation early! As for tokens of affection, remember that garish extravagances are the province of the very young. A simple card, sincere and unadorned, and a discreet Rolex are always good gifts to give or to receive. Keep plenty of vases on hand. A crushed aspirin will prolong the life of your flowers. Don't concern yourself in the slightest about getting a date. Someone will turn up.

tric egg beater my mother had given me—along with a toaster and a decent set of pots and pans—the year I left home: the year before C. came along. She never suspected I would put her thoughtful gift to the nefarious purposes of that drunken, flesh-ridden summer. I thought of her as I removed the beaters from their moorings, banged them against the bowl to knock off the excess, and began, tentatively at first, to lick away the cream that remained, holding those beaters, one in each fist, enjoying the press of their firm cold stems along the tell-all lines of my palms, touching my tongue slowly, delicately, to the random sculptings of that liquid gone firm, first one beater, then the other, slipping my tongue around and along and up and down those four thin and curved, grooved and silver ribs, one, then the other, the sharp tang of the metal under the sweet white, remembering doing this very thing as a child, begging my mother to allow me to do it, Sunday afternoons before supper, some kind of chiffon pie in the fridge and my father watching *Hymn Sing* in the living room, this was our little ritual, my mother handing me the beaters, one, then the other, my child's tongue, and oh, the cream, remembering a hot jealousy when my brothers craved and received this same favour, remembering all this, licking faster and more purposefully now, all concern for propriety gone, sucking even, investigating every remote and hidden crevice, probing the hard axis, the remote hubs, first one, then the other, remembering C. and that sultry afternoon, August, remembering I was twenty-two, remembering C. was my present age and is now sixty, remembering the house in the orchard and the horse at the window and the sour waft of

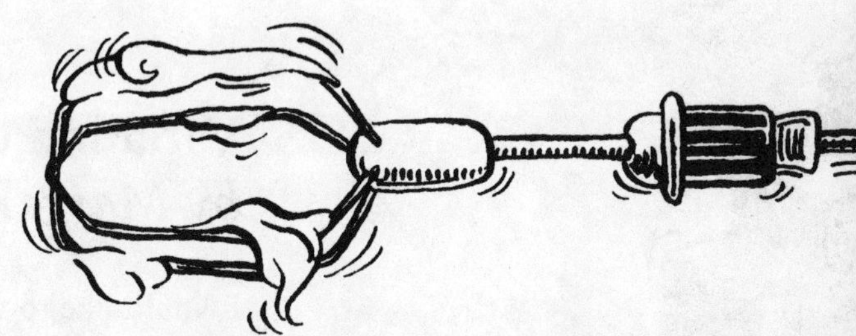

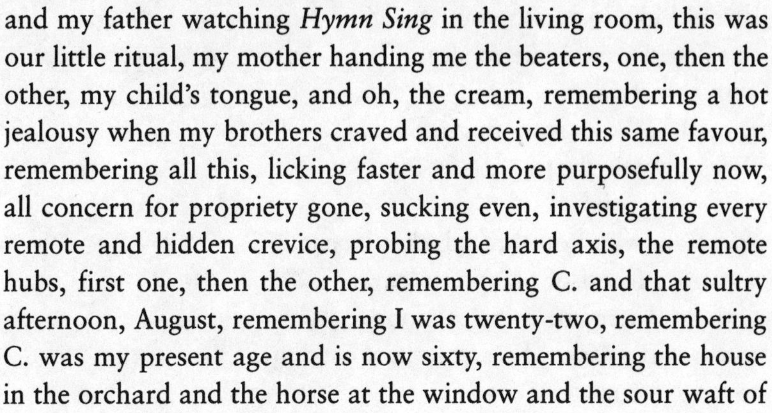

the cream and the acrid alarm of the surprised stink bugs who seemed to live under the pillows of all damn places, remembering the shuddering, the sundering, first one, then the other, then good-bye, and then it's the same old story, it's done and there's nothing left but restlessness and disappointment, first one, then the other, and what can you do but go on living in your changing body and carry out the business of getting older? Which is what I did. Am doing. First one, then the other.

Pardon? The pie? Oh, it was fine, just fine, thanks for asking, though I should have used a touch more vanilla in the cream.

Variation on the word *sleep*
by Margaret Atwood

I would like to watch you sleeping,
which may not happen.
I would like to watch you,
sleeping. I would like to sleep
with you, to enter
your sleep as its smooth dark wave
slides over my head

and walk with you through that lucent
wavering forest of bluegreen leaves
with its water sun & three moons
towards the cave where you must descend,
towards your worst fear

I would like to give you the silver
branch, the small white flower, the one
word that will protect you
from the grief at the center
of your dream, from the grief
at the center. I would like to follow
you up the long stairway
again & become
the boat that would row you back
carefully, a flame
in two cupped hands
to where your body lies
beside me, and you enter
it as easily as breathing in

I would like to be the air
that inhabits you for a moment
only. I would like to be that unnoticed
& that necessary.

Hector: The Same Old Canard

I have a jackdaw's propensity to gather up bright and shiny things and cart them home. "You can never tell when it might come in handy" is my byword when I waltz through the kitchen door, bearing my treasures and remnants: a doll's head or a scythelike shard of pottery, a table leg or a hubcap. Virgil will arch his right eyebrow, wipe his hands on his apron and purse his lips ever so slightly, all of which I recognize as signals of mild disapprobation.

"Why yes," he might say, "only yesterday I was looking for a rusted canary cage and couldn't find one." Every so often he must vent his genial disdain by tossing out so deliberately fatuous a riposte. By and large, however, he manages to suppress his skepticism. We long ago learned that the path to domestic harmony is paved with tolerance for one another's foibles and peccadilloes. He withholds sniping at me for my packrat tendencies—at least, until the accumulation starts to verge on a fire-hazard situation. He mostly overlooks my vanity and would never dream of smirking when I confine myself to my room for an hour to try out one of Altona's facial masques. Similarly, I withhold comment when Virgil has one of his periodic Edith Piaf sing-along marathons, even when "Les Trois Cloches" or "Milord" kicks in for perhaps the tenth time in a row. And only once, when I was feeling frayed around the edges, did I allow that it sets my nerves on edge to hear him slurping his soup. It took a week for him to lose the wounded look.

It's the randomness of scavenging that pleases me. When I go out on the rambles from which I sometimes return encumbered, I don't have such dross-gathering specifically in mind. It's just that

when I see a bottle of cerulean hue winking at me in the long grass, or when I spy from the corner of my eye a picture frame discarded on the shoulder of the road, I am invaded by an irrational joy. It is as though I have been sent a reminder that the world is full of surprises for those who will only see them. "Hello, little one," I will murmur to the foundling as I gather it into my arms, "how came you here? Come with me, I'll give you a good home." By the time I've made it back to the house, we will have bonded and nothing could come between us.

I attribute my success in this recuperative work to the operations of destiny rather than free will. Although I am not above lifting the lid of a promising trash tin and having a discreet poke through, I prefer to leave the discovery of my trinkets to chance. There is something unwholesome, to my way of thinking, about making a point of seeking out such treasures. I am reminded of one of our recent guests, who put into port with his metal detector. I had never seen such a gizmo before, and he showed me how it worked by passing it over his skull, onto which a considerate surgeon had riveted a postoperative steel plate. This demented demonstration proved to be his favourite party piece, for he performed it again the next morning for the assembled household at the breakfast table. Perceiving me somehow as a kindred spirit, he invited me to accompany him down to the seashore for some high-tech beachcombing, and dutifully I went along. He trudged along the tideline, impervious to the beauty and music of the sea, dowsing the sand with his sensitive wand, listening through his headset for the tell-tale beeping, crowing with pleasure every time he found a screw or washer or scrap of foil.

"Is it money you're after?" I asked him as we made our way home.

"What? Like buried pirate booty? Ha! That's a good one! No, weeks go by and I won't uncover so much as a nickel. I just do it to pass the time. And every so often I find a bottle opener. I collect them, you know."

"Bottle openers?"

"Why, sure! I've got over five hundred in my basement, all shapes and sizes! There's a fascinating history to bottle openers!" Which he then proceeded to relate in such numbing detail that I half wondered if his metal plate wasn't picking up signals from another astral plane.

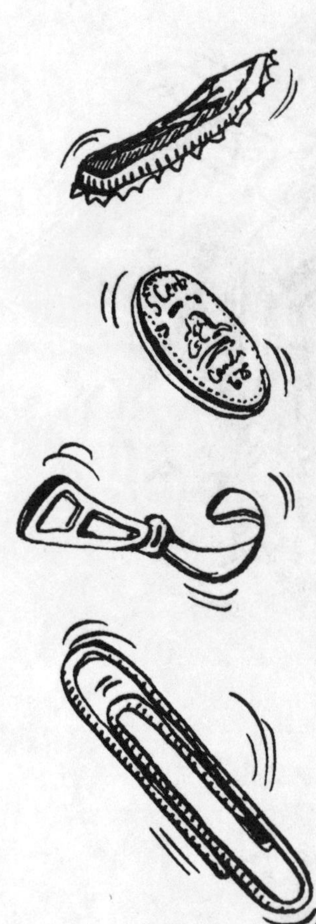

I would never dispute that I have hoarding tendencies. However, the lobe of the brain that governs the urge to amass one specialized item—such as bottle openers—is either absent from my physiognomy or else it long ago atrophied. Philately and numismatics hold not the slightest attraction for me. Ear trumpets, corkscrews, theatre programmes, thimbles, vintage recordings of Caruso, D. H. Lawrence first editions, ashtrays, swizzle sticks, eighteenth-century surgical tools: all these objects, and any others you might care to name, are adored and zealously tracked down by people of conventional mien who are in most other ways wholly normal. It is a sensibility I am able to accommodate in others easily enough but have never shared. Therefore, it is more than slightly ironic that the deceased Donald Craven—roughly seventy years of age, late of Seattle, Washington, who was once and once only a visitor to the Bachelor Brothers' Bed & Breakfast—should have decided that I, Hector, was the very one unto whom he should consign his unusual—and it must be said, grotesque—flock of twenty stuffed mallards.

There was no note from a solicitor. We learned of this bequest only when his widow—an attractive woman in her forties who carried herself with the bearing of one who has latterly realized that her best years lie ahead of her—came up our drive of an afternoon, piloting a station wagon into which that ghastly cargo had been shoehorned, tail to bill.

"I was worried about whether they'd hassle me at the border," she said as she began to offload the things onto the porch, "but they never so much as blinked."

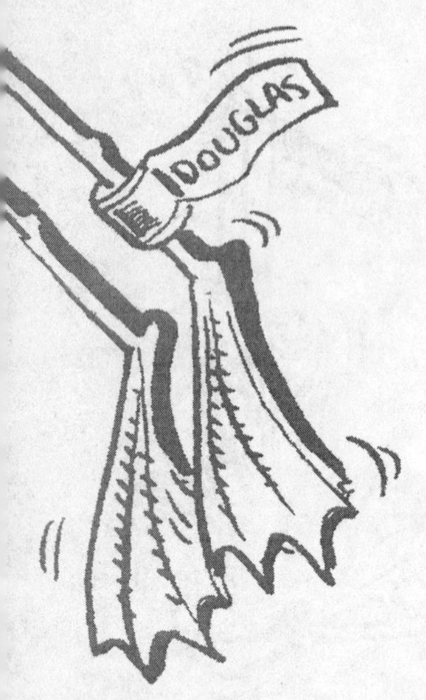

"Are you sure there isn't some mistake?" I picked up one of the ducks and squinted into its glassy, uncomprehending eyes. I noticed there was a band with the name "Douglas" on one of its legs.

"No mistake at all," she answered, handing fowl after fowl to the equally bewildered Virgil. "He said very specifically that this was the place he wanted the ducks to go. Don't ask me why. It was one of his dying wishes. I guess he thought you'd be the types to appreciate them."

"Oh, that does speak well of us!" were the words that emanated from my brother's corner, though I'm not sure whether he articulated them or just thought them loud enough for me to hear.

"Douglas?" I asked, for I could think of nothing else to say save "thank you," which hardly seemed apt.

"He named them all after his children and grandchildren. Douglas is his eldest son, my stepson. None of them are mine, in fact. I'm the third wife. The first two had to do all the hard work. I just had to look after burying him. Which was a breeze, relatively speaking."

Keith, Bert, Wayne, Wally, Patricia, Irene, Floyd, David, Diana, Sue, Donald Jr., Michael, Lois, Tiffany, Chelsea, Elaine, Brent, Summer, and Cheyenne had soon joined Douglas on the stoop. They were brightly coloured or dunnish and drab, depending on the hand dealt them by gender. Each was identical in its dull posture of permanence. None of them held their wings aloft or spread. No heads were tossed back, saucy or exultant. It was impossible to read in any of their faces anything that might even be mistaken for surprise. No, they simply stood at their ease, all twenty of them, lined up and peaceable, all facing the same way, as though queuing for a bus that was sure to arrive any minute now.

"Do you mind my asking how," I stammered, "that is to say, in what way . . . I mean, did he . . ."

"Shoot them?" she asked, seizing my inarticulate question by the scruff and giving it a hearty shake. "God, no. Donald never shot anything in his life. He'd have been a hazard with a gun, what with his astigmatism and all. No, they all just fell from the sky one day and landed in our yard. I'll never forget it. I heard this thudding, looked out the window, and there they were, just pelting down. They were frozen solid, too. At first I thought some passing plane must have been in trouble and discharged its cargo. But evidently not. It's a natural phenomenon. You read about it in the tabloids, sometimes. There'll be a bunch of birds flying along, geese, pigeons, whatever, all peaceful like, minding their own damn business, following the same old migration routes, when out of nowhere a freak cold front sneaks up, catches them off guard—and whammo! They're dropping like cannon balls. I don't understand the mechanics of it. All I know is that one of them put a thousand-dollar dent in the hood of my Toyota and that Donald figured it was the most miraculous thing that ever happened to him. He went out there and gathered them all up and put them in the freezer and started calling every taxidermist

in the book. Even when he was ill, he was a great comparison shopper. Oh here," she said, opening the trunk, "I thought you might like these, too."

And then she drove away, leaving me holding a huge rack of moose antlers—the provenance of which we can only guess—and Virgil sitting stunned among the twenty mallards. I would have been hard-pressed to say who looked more forlorn, man or bird.

"So fair and fowl a day I ne'er have seen," I quipped, to no good effect.

"Toil and trouble," Virgil muttered, picking up Donald Jr. "Do you in fact remember Donald Craven? Who was he? Whatever did we do to deserve being named his beneficiaries?"

When we first opened our house to paying guests as a bed and breakfast, I had imagined that each and every one of our visitors would leave an indelible impression. While many have done just that, there are others—especially those who came only once and stayed for a short time and did nothing extraordinary or untoward—who are buried beyond retrieval in the bottom drawer of memory. It took a bit of leafing through the grey matter files, but I finally was able to put a face to Mr. Craven. He was on his way elsewhere when he fell victim to a wrong left turn and turned up on our doorstep, unannounced, in the first year of our operation. We were able to take him in for the one night he required.

It was Mrs. Rochester who made his visit so memorable. He was fascinated, as are so many of our guests, with the parrot. At the time of his visit she was going through a Beatrix Potter phase and was disgorging from her brain and beak excerpts from her favourite stories.

"'*I will get some worms and go fishing and catch a dish of minnows for my dinner,' said Mr. Jeremy Fisher.*"

"Little Benjamin said, 'It spoils people's clothes to squeeze under a gate; the proper way to get in, is to climb down a pear tree.'"

"The waistcoat is cut out from peach-coloured satin—tambour stitch and rose-buds in beautiful floss-silk. Was I wise to entrust my last four-pence to Simpkin? One-and-twenty button-holes of cherry-coloured twist!"

And so on.

Mr. Craven was impressed, as well he might have been. Mrs. Rochester is a very uncommon bird.

"Clever Polly!" he crowed. "How old is she?"

"Of my three score years and ten, twenty will not come again," was her own cryptic answer.

"We don't really know," I told him. "Older than we, that's for sure."

"And Moses went and spake these words unto all Israel. And he said unto them, I am an hundred and twenty years old this day; I can no more go out and come in: also the Lord hath said unto me, Thou shalt not go over this Jordan."

"My goodness! She knows the book of Numbers, too!"

"Deuteronomy," corrected the fractious Mrs. R., *"31.1-2."*

"What an extraordinary creature! I hope you'll have her stuffed when she dies!"

This was an improvident and unfortunate remark. Mrs. Rochester believes herself to be among the immortals, and for all I know she may well be. What is sure is that she does not gladly suffer talk of her own demise. She let loose with a volley of her most practised and stinging invective, much of it in Latin. Unfortunately, the phrase *"Get stuffed yourself, four-eyes!"* rang through loud, clear and true.

"Ah," said Virgil, petting Irene on the head. "So that's the

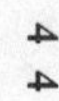

root of the whole *canard*. He harboured a grudge, all that time. It seems an extravagant revenge for so slight an offence."

As for me, I'm not at all sure that revenge was the operative principle. For all we know, he might have been a life-long practical joker. If that is the case, it pleases me to think that he was able to exit laughing. And as it turned out, we were able to disperse our peculiar windfall without any difficulty.

"I'll take those!" cried Altona when she saw the moose antlers. She hauled them home, screwed them into the wall above her vanity table and placed prophylactic, gaily painted styrofoam snowballs on the eye-threatening tips of the spreading rack. The weaponry that once some moose used to defend his honour has been transformed into a necklace tree. And festive it looks, too, all festooned with her many strings of beads.

As for the ducks, we one by one found them suitable homes. Keith, Bert and Diana all went to the local elementary school, where they now occupy a place of pride in the "Marsh and Wetlands" diorama. We make a point of visiting them when we go to the children's gym for a concert or pageant. Wayne and Wally were taken back to the city by a window dresser who felt he could incorporate them into a sock display; we imagined that argyle styles would somehow be prominent. Patricia, Donald Jr. and Chelsea were gladly embraced by an enthusiastic amateur juggler who was looking for new challenges. Lois and Floyd were carted away by a hard-of-hearing gentleman who plays with a seniors' hockey league. He misapprised our question as "Would you by any chance care to take a puck home with you?" and brightly answered that he would gladly relieve us of a couple, if we had them to spare. He was simply too embarrassed to retract his promise.

Rae and June, the proprietors of the Well of Loneliness, installed Tiffany and Summer atop their espresso machine, and changed the rather modish names of their new and feathered tenants to Virginia and Vita. Their daughter, Martina, who recently turned one and is both precocious and eccentric, calls one of them "doggy" and the other "kitty." David and Cheyenne wound up as paperweights on the desks of Abel Wackaugh and J. MacDonald Bellweather II, respectively. Irene, Sue, Douglas and Michael were taken back to Seattle by a woman who teaches still-life drawing classes. It was an inspired choice on her part, as the chances of Irene, Sue, Douglas and Michael ever moving again are remote. Elaine was claimed by Caedmon Harkness, who cleverly installed her as a hood ornament on the thatched schoolbus that he uses both for transportation and housing. Brent we kept. Waffle, our pretty calico, would have it no other way.

Incomprehensible, inexplicable, mysterious, strange, unintelligible, impenetrable, unaccountable: these are the adjectives my thesaurus supplies when I look up the word "inscrutable." None seems to measure up to the task of getting under the rock of a cat's whys and wherefores. Ah, Waffle! Who could look into the yellow-grey flames that serve her for eyes and divine her occult meanings, her secret intentions, her arcane and esoteric longings? What is it that moves her to suddenly leap from her basket and career up and down the stairs, pausing only on the landing to chase her own tail in a moment of kittenish exuberance? What process of assessment does she run when she struts into the library and finds it full of our guests, each one absorbed in a book, each one with a lap on which she might splay? Only one sitter will be accorded the honour, and the reason that she or he will be selected is always Waffle's own, that no one could ever

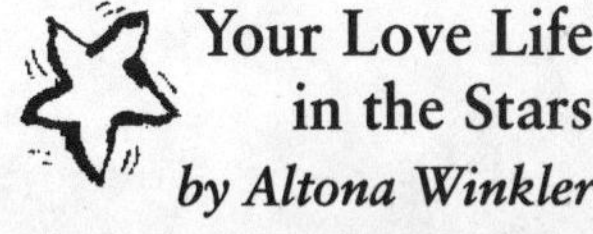

Your Love Life in the Stars

by Altona Winkler

PISCES

February 19 to March 20

Poor Pisces! You find yourself in the throes of a moral dilemma. You are presently dating three people, and you wonder if this is right and proper. Of course it is! It only becomes difficult if they all find out about the others and get hot under the collar as a consequence. But with some careful planning and artful tale-telling, you should be able to avoid such an eventuality. Be sure you get plenty of sleep, however. You'll need to keep up your energy!

guess and that she will never divulge. And who could suppose that Waffle would walk onto the porch, mere minutes after the Widow Craven had squealed her tires at the end of our drive, scrutinize the newly arrived flock of twenty mallards, and fall deeply, deeply, in love with Brent?

"I wonder," speculated Virgil, "if he might have been stuffed with catnip." It was not an unreasonable conclusion, for there was no doubt that Brent's effect on our puss was markedly narcotic. She stepped over and around Elaine and Irene and Douglas and all the rest and went straight for him. A deep purr rose from the pit of her chest, a sexy throb and rumble, as Waffle circled the unresistant Brent. She rubbed her cheeks and jowls liberally over his puckered breast, rolled on her back and grabbed at his bill from beneath, every now and then emitting a yowl of something that was either pleasure or astonishment or both. Lying supine, she wrapped her forelegs around the duck's neck and held on, tight. "Eeeoarrrghhnnnnyooowwwwhrrrrrrrrrrrmmmmmmm," she whispered into his mallard ear as she toppled him to the floor and proceeded to roll all over him. One of his pin feathers came free of its moorings, and she batted it happily into the air.

"Are we sure she was fixed?" asked Virgil, who blushed to see this display of intense, interspecies devotion.

"Atta girl," said Altona, when she came by later that night, and Waffle and Brent were still entangled. "Get the upper hand and keep it! It's always worked for me!" Then it was my turn to get red of cheek.

That was months ago. Brent now lives atop a disused gramophone casing that found a new life as a liquor cabinet. Though Waffle is no longer as obsessive about him as she was when he first came to stay—by which I mean to say she is not at his side twenty-four hours a day—she is still powerfully fond of him. Once, when I can only suppose they had had a lover's spat, she cuffed him soundly, hissed and flounced off in deepest umbrage. But she was back to make amends before the day was done. I would say the honeymoon is far from over.

We have a pair of real honeymooners under our roof just now. They are our age, more or less, and neither has been married before. To come across people in their fifties who are getting hitched for the first time is almost as rare a thing as discovering two bachelor brothers who choose to live together in the same house in which they were born and raised. This happy couple met through a newspaper ad—information they were quick to share, so I don't feel I am betraying any confidences—and experienced a full-fledged *coup de foudre* at first sight.

"And we arranged to meet for the first time at a McDonald's!" she explained. "Can you imagine? It was my suggestion. I liked him on the phone, but I wasn't willing to get my hopes up until I'd laid eyes on him, too. What if he was covered head to toe with serpent tattoos? There are limits, even when you're over fifty. I thought I'd be better equipped to handle the disappointment in a bland, plastic environment rather than a cosy restaurant with flowers and candles all over the place. You know, the kind of place where you'd like to linger. As it turned out, we spent three hours sitting in a booth next to a six-year-old's birthday party, talking and talking and talking. And I knew. I just knew. We both did."

What a wonderful thing! To have lived more than half a lifetime, to be of an age when one can fully expect to look up and see the standards of cynicism and disappointment flying from every parapet, yet still to be able to embrace, unconditionally and without reserve, the certainty that here is a person with whom you can be more wholly yourself than you have been, all these years living on your own.

"He brought me to the banqueting house, and his banner over me was love," intoned Mrs. Rochester when these middle-aged sweethearts came down to their first breakfast with us. *"The Song of Solomon, 2.4."*

"Why, Mrs. Rochester," I said, amazed at her gentility, "a kindly bird like you we'll want to keep around. We might just have you stuffed and mounted after all."

"Fuck off," she muttered, *sotto voce*, so as not to offend our visitors. And with a wink of her sharp green eye, she grabbed a wedge of peach from a fruit nappy and scuttled out of the kitchen, cackling with glee at her own cunning and indomitability, cackling without a trace of charity shining in her old harridan heart. Which is as it should be. Which is the world as we know it.

Caedmon's Saint of the Month: March

St. Frances, whose feast day is March 9, was born in Rome in 1384. Even as a child, she demonstrated that she was full of the stuff of holiness, eschewing games and amusements for long hours of solitary prayer and rudimentary mortifications. She would have been the ideal sister, always willing to cede the bigger piece of pie to a sibling of lower spiritual degree.

She wanted most desperately to become a nun. Alas, her parents compelled her to marry, at the age of thirteen, a rich young power broker called Lorenzo Ponziano. She founded a religious order, which she was unable to join until Lorenzo was dead, freeing her to embrace chastity with the same enthusiasm she had already shown for poverty and obedience. She died in 1440.

Pius XI named Frances the patron saint of motorists. Why she received this assignment is not entirely clear, although it might have to do with the fact that she had an unusually close relationship with her guardian angel. Evidently, they were in constant visual contact. Who better to ensure that we keep our eyes on the straight and narrow road ahead?

The little devotion below to Frances remarks her legendary kindness to her servants. Rev. Alban Butler, the great English chronicler of saints, tells us that she treated the hired help not with contempt but as co-heirs to the kingdom of heaven. Let us pray.

Dear St. Frances, hear my plea,
Let my boss be good to me.
Let him see that kindness pays:
Ergo, then, a yearly raise,
Holidays in three-week spans,
And a decent dental plan,
Pension payments that accrue,
Coffee breaks are peachy, too.
Thanks, St. Frances, late of Rome.
Come again, and safe drive home!

Our Guests Write: Alan

Dear Hector and Virgil:

Home again, home again. I made it to back to Thunder Bay in three days. Were I not so obsessed with the need for eight hours of sleep a night, or if I'd had the right pills, I could have been here sooner. When I was awake, however, I was driving. Every now and then, I'd pull over to stretch my legs or swill a cup of truck-stop coffee. I didn't take in any of the sights or points of historical interest, although I did pause for a reflective moment on the flat sweep of the prairies to remember the first of two occasions on which I've seen my mother scared. That was the day she almost killed us all: my brothers, our father, herself and me, all in one fell swoop, in Saskatchewan.

I was ten. We were on a camping holiday, destination Victoria. Mom was at the wheel. She was a good driver, comfortable with the tedious urban hither and yon of grocery shopping and attending meetings, well-practised at chauffeuring her brood to and from swimming lessons and orthodontist appointments. But she was a novice on the highway. A long flat ribbon of steamy asphalt. Several tons of Dodge. And 60 m.p.h. Here were three balls she had never thought of juggling.

Somewhere near Regina, she pulled out to pass on a two-lane stretch and found herself playing chicken with an oncoming truck. She cranked hard left, aimed the car at the gravel shoulder, and brought it to a halt in a dry and mercifully shallow ditch. There was no visible damage to the Dodge, and none to us. In fact, we three boys, preadolescent and self-absorbed and resilient, were thrilled with the heart-lurching ride. It was better than the roller coaster at the fair! We began to babble straight away about how we couldn't wait to get to Victoria and tell our grandparents about our close brush with death!

It was only our mother's chalky face and her quiet insistence that we keep the news of this little detour to ourselves that made us understand something of the gravity of the situation. She moved to the passenger seat. Dad took us the rest of the way to the coast and all the way back home. She didn't drive again for thirty years. And that was the first time I saw her scared.

The second time was three years ago, in the hospital, on the night before her mastectomy. The cancer had been found in a haphazard way. A few weeks after her retirement, when she was in a mood to do some of the things she'd been putting off for thirty-five years, she went to the doctor. Over the course of a routine medical, her physician found a lump my mother had never noticed, or else had discounted as trivial. The biopsy told its nasty tale. Surgery was scheduled.

She didn't say much in the day or two before the operation. She said, "For Pete's sake! My mother lost both breasts. I should have been paying more attention." She said, "Mammograms! I'd like to see a man get his balls checked over by one of those things!" And in the hospital, on the night before the surgery, she said with uncharacteristic candour, "I'm scared."

I was visited by an uneasy memory, then. Myself, age eight. A cool, grey afternoon. The hospital. And a tonsillectomy slated for the morning, the prospect of which was barely mitigated by the promise of endless vats of ice cream. That was back in my mother's driving days, and it had fallen to her to deliver me up for the slaughter. She rooted around in her handbag for her keys when it was time for her to leave. I said, "I'm scared."

"You'll be fine," she said. "You'll be fine."

And naturally, she was right. But what words could I find to comfort her as she prepared to enlist needfully and unhappily in that army in which so many women now march? "You'll be fine?" No. This was a sure enough prophecy for her to have made, way back then when I was still a child and fear had not yet tracked her down. Now it made no sense. She knew that I knew that no one knew how much stupid damage had been done by the disaffected, delinquent cells. What do you say when, for the first time in your adult life, you feel like a parent to your parent?

"I'm scared," she said.

"Me too."

Outside her room, the city. Beyond the city, the prairie, mountains at the margin. Somewhere on the other side, the future packed his furtive bags. Three years later, my mother would be active and healthy and, so far, knock on wood, cancer-free. But then, of course, the outcome was wholly obscure. In that moment, we were just scared grownups, looking all at once into the face of something very big and very dangerous, perilously near, thundering along a random, crazy path, coming at us very fast.

Yours,

Alan Gauthier, Thunder Bay, Ontario

From *Peter Pan*
by J. M. Barrie

It is the nightly custom of every good mother after her children are asleep to rummage in their minds and put things straight for next morning, repacking into their proper places the many articles that have wandered during the day. If you could keep awake (but of course you can't) you would see your own mother doing this, and you would find it very interesting to watch her. It is quite like tidying up drawers. You would see her on her knees, I expect, lingering humorously over some of your contents, wondering where on earth you had picked this thing up, making discoveries sweet and not so sweet, pressing this to her cheek as if it were a nice kitten and hurriedly stowing that out of sight. When you wake in the morning, the naughtiness and evil passions with which you went to bed have been folded up small and placed at the bottom of your mind; and on the top, beautifully aired, are spread out your prettier thoughts, ready for you to put on.

Caedmon: Found in the Potting Shed

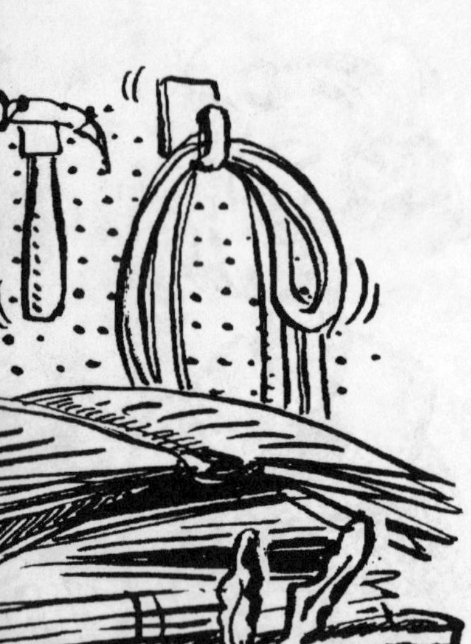

I was out in the potting shed, checking to see that all was in readiness for the spring planting, and found a pile of old magazines. This is the kind of diversion I can never resist. I sat down and had a flip-through. In one of these periodicals—and this was ironic, considering the venue—I found an article about Beatrix Potter. It was written by a British psychiatrist, and in it he attests that Squirrel Nutkin—the eponymous protagonist in one of her tiny, perfect children's nature tales—suffers from Tourette's syndrome. He observed that while Twinkleberry and the other bushy-tailed rodents are hard-working and assiduous, Nutkin is given to disruptive behaviours and inappropriate expostulations. "Hum-a-bum! buzz! buzz! Hum-a-bum buzz!" he will exclaim, while dancing up and down "like a sunbeam." He also engages in obsessive, repetitive activities and makes odd whirring noises. Casebook Tourette's, *n'est-ce pas?*

Most readers of such a news item, particularly if they are fond of Beatrix Potter, will roll their eyes heavenward and dismiss these shrink-wrapped insights as yet another instance of the evils of the publish-or-perish imperative. However, I have gone back and examined Potter's oeuvre, mostly published between the turn of the century and the First World War, and I can report that she was astonishingly insightful and anticipatory of many of the psychosocial issues and controversies that now tumble about the pages of behaviourist, sociological and medical literature. Indeed, it is becoming increasingly clear that Beatrix Potter was not just a kindly woman with a fondness for observing the ways of rabbits, mice and barnyard animals, but a visionary, a radical, a seer, a moralist and an iconoclast who left a rich legacy of protorevolutionary writing, overbrimming with cautionary wisdom. It's all there for those who have eyes to see. To illustrate this point, let us peer between the lines of some of her artful fables.

Consider *The Tale of Mrs. Tiggy-Winkle*. Superficially, this is the quaint story of the meeting between a stout washerwoman and a girl called Lucie, who is searching for her mislaid handkerchiefs and pinafore. But scratch the surface of this simple tale, and you will find the far-seeing Potter's warning against the terrible dangers of drug abuse. Carefully deconstructing her text, we see that Potter intended Lucie—whose name, after all, means light—as the embodiment of innocence in peril. Directly she enters Mrs. Tiggy-Winkle's dark hillside workroom, where the laundress is ostensibly ironing, Lucie notices "a hot singey smell," an odour familiar to anyone who has ever stumbled into a crack den while looking for change for the gum machine. Furthermore, we are told that Mrs. Tiggy-Winkle's "little black nose went sniffle, sniffle, snuffle, and her eyes went twinkle, twinkle." Those who have witnessed the effect of cocaine use will recognize these indicators as certain signs that everything is not on the up-and-up with the genial Mrs. T! Any doubt about Potter's deeper motivations is cast off in the closing pages of the book, when Mrs. Tiggy-Winkle strips off her clothes and is proven to be a hedgehog, *covered in needles*. Potter's bright warning shines though the anthropomorphic conventions of children's literature, leaving us only with the hope that the vile Mrs. Tiggy-Winkle thought to use her laundry bleach to sterilize her syringes before reusing or sharing them.

There's much more to be divined from the Potter canon, once you know where and how to look. For instance, in *Mr. Jeremy*

The Twelve Months

Snowy, Flowy, Blowy,
Showery, Flowery, Bowery,
Hoppy, Croppy, Droppy,
Breezy, Sneezy, Freezy.

Fisher, Potter is full of astonishingly prescient advice about what we now call safe sex. Mr. Jeremy Fisher, a bachelor frog, goes down to the pond for an afternoon of trolling. He sensibly wears his macintosh and galoshes. A trout seizes him but finds the taste of protective coating so off-putting that he spits out the well-wrapped frog. In other words, Mr. Jeremy Fisher was saved by wearing rubbers.

In *The Tale of Peter Rabbit,* Potter foretells the rudiments of sociobiology and anticipates the very recently published research which posits that compulsive novelty seekers owe their behaviour in large measure to a surfeit of a chemical disinhibitor called dopamine, which they are, in effect, programmed to produce. Peter's siblings, Flopsy, Mopsy and Cottontail, who are "good little bunnies," heed their mother's warning not to go in Mr. McGregor's garden. Peter, however, cannot help himself. Evidently, he inherited his restlessness from his father, who perished during just such a raid and was baked in a pie. Despite this, Peter tempts fate by encroaching on the farmer's turf. Ever the moralist, Potter makes no attempt to excuse the delinquent rabbit's conduct. She is clear that although our behaviour may owe something to our genetic mix, we must still be held accountable for our actions. Hence, Peter's famous humiliation: he is sent to bed with a dose of chamomile tea.

Finally, *The Tale of Jemima Puddle Duck* is a highly charged tract about the need for family planning. You will recall how Jemima Puddle Duck is not allowed to hatch her own eggs. Rather, they are given to a hen who is a more reliable brooder. Distraught, Jemima devises a plan to nest on her eggs away from the barnyard and very nearly runs afoul of a fox. Thanks to the intervention of Kep the collie, who represents wisdom, she is saved from the whiskered villain, who symbolizes untrammelled fertility. In the end, Jemima manages to become the happy mother of four wee ones, which should be enough for any one duck.

Beatrix Potter lived a long and fruitful life but is only now gaining the recognition she deserves as an activist, prophet, social critic and tactician. As Pigling Bland, Miss Moppet, Tom Kitten, the Tailor of Gloucester and all the others begin to surrender their secrets, we can expect see Beatrix Potter in all her glory, revealed to us as what she is, was and always will be: a writer for now, for then and for the dawning millennium.

Our Guests Write: Mason

Dear Hector and Virgil:
In recent weeks, I've been lucky enough to travel to places where I've seen ice. Two weeks ago I was in St. John's, and the harbour was thick with the stuff, farmed out by various bergs. Sea gulls dived in their numbers into the narrow channels sculpted out by the colonizing floes and seemed to come up lucky. Last weekend, I walked over the Broadway Bridge in Saskatoon, through a punishing wind, and noted how the Saskatchewan River was beginning to ooze up as the scab of crusty water gave way. The ice that remained had a pocked and leprous cast to it; a wasted, *ancien régime* look. You could tell it wasn't long for this world, that the undermining influences of sun and flow were whittling away at its between-the-banks hegemony and would soon send it packing.

Here, on the West Coast, spring comes on quickly with a sluttish show of bloomers. One morning, you wake up sneezing and know it's arrived. On the prairies, and elsewhere in the country, you measure its inch-by-inch progress by studying the retreating ice, which is the necessary prelude to the greening of the world. I can't say I've been seized by an overwhelming sense of nostalgia for that slow vernal shift, which is the one I knew growing up. To be perfectly frank, I've come to prefer the sudden pyrotechnics of the cherry trees and rhododendrons. Still, having seen and smelled once again the measured march of that other, more stubborn spring—especially after so many years of witnessing the season as an explosion of one breathtaking tree after another—I have to say that I am, for the first time in many years, feeling connected to Eastertime.

I am not, in any literal sense of the word, a Christian. I don't attend church, and I don't subscribe to the specific tenets of faith that would give me the right or obligation to name myself as one. Nonetheless, it's the religious and moral tradition in which I was raised, and there are still moments when I feel that same tidal tug of mystery I knew as a child, when I would listen to accounts of the death and resurrection of Jesus, in all their grim and gripping detail: denial, betrayal, the nails, the cross, the weeping mother, the mocking crowds, the blackened sky, the hard words: Gethsemane, Golgotha. I would hear these things with a chill of dread, and I'd puzzle over the aftermath. Back from the dead after three days? How could such things be? There was freedom to be found in simply accepting that it was so.

This was before I gave myself over to the secular humanism that became my guiding light. This was before I decided to see that marvellous story as a story; as a powerful emblem of human hope and suffering, rather than as a literal truth in every word of its telling. I have no quarrel with anyone who believes otherwise and no interest in luring anyone into my camp. I'm only saying that this, rather too simply stated, is what I've come to believe. I will admit that while it satisfies my head, it leaves my heart wanting. And when an absent heart strips holy days of their emotional resonance, you stop paying them much mind.

This year, somehow, my mild adventures around the ice have added a new charge to the Easter season. I think it has to do with the visible evidence of resurrection. I think it has to do with being there to see the stone rolled back and life issuing forth. I think it has to do with being on the prairies and looking up at that vast expanse of sky just in time to see it punctuated by a strange diacritical mark, like a ragged circumflex, moving north across the blue. You say to yourself, "Oh no, this can't be. This is almost too painful to bear." But sure enough, there they are. Geese. They're too high up for you to hear their raucous hymn, but not so far away that you can't watch them drift in and out of formation, now an S, now an L, and just for a moment they approximate a cross, before they remember who they are and veer off on their practised route, leaving you with the fleeting sense that there is still a place in the world for miracles, and if only you could have read between their lines, you could have had one, there and then.
Mason Logan, Powell River, B.C.

Some Shrovetide Notes

Although we are neither of us much given to such Lenten traditions as the abandonment of some favourite comestible, we do like to observe Shrove Tuesday by serving our guests and ourselves a big feed of pancakes. Truth be told, we have come to rely on a commercial mix for our feast of fritters. However, for those of you who abhor such culinary cheating, here are the reliable Miss Acton's "Observations on Omelettes, Pancakes, Fritters, &c.":

There is no difficulty in making good omelettes, pancakes, or fritters; and as they may be expeditiously prepared and served, they are often a very convenient resource when, on short notice, an addition is required to a dinner. The eggs for all of them should be well and lightly whisked; the lard for frying batter should be extremely pure in flavour, and quite hot when the fritters are dropped in; the batter itself should be smooth as cream, and it should be briskly beaten the instant before it is used. All fried pastes should be perfectly drained from the fat before they are served, and sent to table promptly when they are ready. Make a light batter of eggs, flour, and milk; a little salt, nutmeg, and ginger may be added; fry in a small pan, in hot dripping lard. Sugar and lemon should be served to eat with them. Or, when eggs are scarce, make the batter with small beer, ginger, and so forth; or water, with flour, and a very little milk will serve, but not so much as eggs and all milk.

3 Rhymes for Pancake Tuesday

Great A, little A,
This is Pancake day;
Toss the ball high,
Throw the ball low,
Those that come after
May sing Heigh-ho!

Pitt a patt, a pan's hot,
I am come to scroving,
Lard's scarce, flour's dear,
That what makes me come
to scroving here,
Eggs in the trencher,
Bacon in the pan,
Ale in the cellar,
And I can carry the can.
As black as a rook,
As speckled as a pie,
I cannot longer sing,
My throat is so dry.

Nicka, nicka, nan;
Give me some pancakes and I'll be gone.
But if you give me none,
I'll throw a great stone,
And down your doors shall come.

Upstairs, Downstairs, in Our Nightgowns

When strangers sleep together under a relatively small roof, and when they meet in the morning for breakfast, a peculiar intimacy settles onto the group. Perhaps they feel safe in the knowledge of their transience, secure that their morning companions are folk they will never meet again and, therefore, it harms nothing to open up a confessional vein. Indeed, there is plainly something therapeutic and necessary in the kind of bean-spilling that often goes on around our breakfast table. You would be surprised how often the subject of bedclothes comes up, and we have long since learned that we can never second-guess who is most or least likely to sleep in the buff. It is true, however, as a general rule, that our older guests are the more likely to speak lovingly of flannel. Here are some words of counsel from that inestimable volume *Enquire Within Upon Everything* about dressing for the sack:

The perfection of dress, for day or night, where warmth is the purpose, is that which confines around the body sufficient of its own warmth, while it allows escape to the exhalations of the skin. Where the body is allowed to bathe protractedly in its own vapours we must expect an unhealthy effect upon the skin. Where there is too little ventilating escape, insensible perspiration is checked, and something analogous to fever supervenes; foul tongue, ill taste, and lack of appetite betray the evil. We know not of anything attended with more serious consequences than that of sleeping in damp linen. Persons are frequently assured that they have been at a fire for many hours, but the question is as to what sort of fire, and whether they have been properly turned, so that

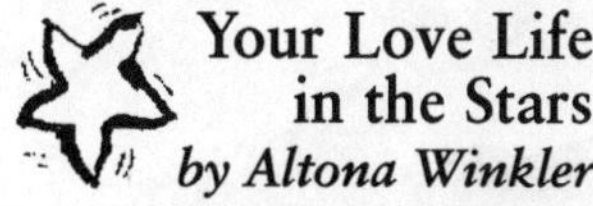

Your Love Life in the Stars

by Altona Winkler

ARIES

March 21 to April 19

An old flame rekindles, Aries! This could prove problematic if you have a new flame alight. Make sure you have your priorities in order. Who do you want to have on the back burner, and who do you want to have on the front? Who do you want to have on simmer, and who do you want to have at a full, frothy boil? And can you really stir two pots at the same time? Hmmmmm?

every part may be exposed to the fire. The fear of creasing the linen, we know, prevents many from unfolding it, so as to be what we consider sufficiently aired; but health is of more importance than appearance: with gentleness there need be no fear of want of neatness.

Disillusionment of Ten O'Clock
by Wallace Stevens

The houses are haunted
By white night-gowns.
None are green,
Or purple with green rings,
Or green with yellow rings,
Or yellow with blue rings.
None of them are strange,
With socks of lace
And beaded ceintures.
People are not going
To dream of baboons and periwinkles.
Only here and there, an old sailor,
Drunk and asleep in his boots,
Catches tigers
In red weather.

May We Recommend: The Bachelor Brothers' List of Bedtime Reading

For a few months after we first opened our bed and breakfast, when we were still wet behind our innkeeping ears and had not settled on the casual aesthetic that now governs this place, we tiptoed around the house after dinner, slipping into each and every guest's room to leave a chocolate on each and every pillow. "Nobody knows the truffles I've seen," Hector would sing, *sotto voce*, as we set out on our crepuscular mission, pussyfooting up and down the stairs and hallways, like calorie-pushing sandmen. It was a sweet touch to be sure, and classy, but we phased it out after one distracted and myopic soul came down to breakfast complaining of hearing loss. Little wonder. He had removed his glasses before crawling into bed, collapsed into sleep and woke in the morning with his ear plugged with chocolate. Now, we personalize each room by leaving a book for bedtime reading on the nightstand. Here is a list of some of our favourites: books about sleep or dreams; books that are episodic and can be read in short spurts; books that can engage the attention of the insomniac or provide a momentary distraction for someone who slips quickly into sleep after just a paragraph or two; books that amuse and divert; books that you might even want to pick up again in the morning.

The Bedside, Bathtub, & Armchair Companion to Agatha Christie edited by Dick Riley and Pam McAllister. Agatha Christie might be old hat and even the object of a certain genial scorn for dyed-in-the-wool, hard-core mystery readers. But even they would have to admit that no one wrote more cosily or cheer-

A Cure for Hiccups

When a twister a-twisting,
will twist him a twist,
For the twisting of his twist,
he three times doth intwist;
But if one of the twines of
the twist do untwist,
The twine that untwisteth,
untwisteth the twist.
Untwirling the twine that
untwisteth between,
He twirls, with the twister,
the two in a twine,
Then twice having twisted
the twines of the twine,
He twisted the twine he had
twined in twain.
The twain, that in twining,
before in the twine,
As twines were intwisted, he
now doth untwine;
'Twixt the twain intertwist-
ing a twine more between.
He, twirling his twister,
makes a twist of the twine.
—Mother Goose

ily about mayhem. In this companion, Christie fans will find such supplementary aids as maps marked with the settings of her books, lists of poisons used to dispatch the innocent, puzzles and quizzes, movie posters, book cover art, and more Dame Agatha trivia than anyone would ever have thought possible or even desirable to squeeze between the covers of a book.

Harem: The World Behind the Veil by Alev Lytle Croutier. A lavishly illustrated peep into the boudoir to end all boudoirs: the seraglio of Topkapi Palace. Of course, there was more to a harem than the bedroom, and the arcane customs and rituals of that rarefied world are lucidly outlined. For instance, we discover that harem women received gifts wrapped in handkerchiefs, the colours of which were full of meaning: red for passionate love, orange for heartache, green for intention, purple for suffering from love, and so on. All told, if you are going to read about handkerchiefs before going to bed, this will serve you far better than, say, *Othello*.

The I Ching, or Book of Changes. We have never been able to figure out exactly how to work this oracle. It may be that we don't have the will to learn. The proper use of the *I Ching* involves the throwing of coins or sticks, and this is exactly the kind of thing we don't want to get into just before bed. Nonetheless, there is comfort and wisdom aplenty to be found in these pages simply by opening them at random. Who could not stand to be reminded, in the minutes before sleep comes on, that "The superior man encourages people at their work, and exhorts them to help one another"?

Night Walks: A Bedside Companion compiled by Joyce Carol Oates. A particularly imaginative collection of nighttime

"Yaup, yaup, yaup!"
Said the croaking voice of a Frog:
"A rainy day
In the month of May,
And plenty of room in the bog."
"Yaup, yaup, yaup!"
Said the Frog, as it hopped away,
"The insects feed
On the floating weed,
And I'm hungry for dinner today."
"Yaup, yaup, yaup!"
Said the Frog, as it splashed about:
"Good neighbours all,
When you hear me call,
It is odd that you do not come out."
"Yaup, yaup, yaup!"
Said the Frog, "it is charming weather
We'll come and sup
When the moon is up—
And we'll all of us croak together."
—Mother Goose

writing assembled by a hugely prolific writer with a particularly gothic turn of mind. Members of the Oatesean college include Dickens, Jean Rhys, Elizabeth Bishop, Carl Jung and Emerson: wildly divergent minds and sensibilities who share with each other, and with us, the joys and terrors of the dark.

The Oxford Book of Dreams chosen by Stephen Brook. We might have chosen any of the marvellous anthologies published by Oxford University Press, but this one seems especially fitting. It's a stew of poems and prose passages selected from novels and essays, as well as from plays, diaries and letters, all having to do with dreams remembered, dreams regretted and dreams interpreted. Some are frightening, some astonishing, some funny. Listening to other people recount their dreams can be a dire and desperate thing, but if you yawn while reading this collection, it won't be from boredom.

Personal Pleasures by Rose Macaulay. What a rare thing it is to find a book devoted wholly to pursuits that make one happy. In 1936, the English writer Dame Rose Macaulay set down her thoughts on pursuits that pleased her personally. They include church-going, armchair sitting, flying, shopping, reading and taking umbrage. They are still fresh and arch all these years later. We think she is especially insightful when she writes about the pleasures of getting into bed and simply remaining there, a luxury to which we all aspire.

Planet and Glow-worm: A Book for the Sleepless compiled by Edith Sitwell. This is a very peculiar and arresting anthology. Given that it was assembled by the peculiar and arresting Dame Edith, who could expect otherwise? This thin volume, which is filled with cullings from writers as diverse as Marco Polo and Gertrude Stein, is "meant for those whose 'continual

He that lies at the stock
Shall have the gold rock;
He that lies at the wall,
Shall have the gold ball;
He that lies in the middle
Shall have the gold fiddle.
—Mother Goose

cares, fears, sorrows, dry brains' drive rest away."

Scorn, with Added Vitriol by Matthew Parris. Parris, a young conservative MP during the years of the Thatcher government, has assembled a "bucketful of discourtesy, disparagement, invective, ridicule, impudence, contumely, derision, hate, affront, disdain, bile, taunts, curses, and jibes." It is very wide-reaching, totally unsparing, frequently cruel and very funny. It's hard not to rejoice with the music critic who had the opportunity and gall to write, "It sounded like as though a pack of rats were being slowly tortured to death, while, from time to time, a dying cow moaned." Steep yourself in this book before going to sleep, and you need never worry about not having an adequate comeback or riposte.

The Wedding Cake in the Middle of the Road: 23 Variations on a Theme edited by Susan Stamberg and George Garrett. Twenty-three writers were invited to wrestle with a single image and concoct a story to be broadcast on a National Public Radio programme. The starting point for each story was the titular wedding cake in the middle of the road. From that unusual and evocative base, writers such as Mary Lee Settle, Joy Williams, David Leavitt, Bharati Mukherjee and Ann Beattie spun off in a great many and unusual directions. It's a book that will amuse and will also change your relationship with baked goods.

Writers Dreaming by Naomi Epel. A series of transcribed radio interviews in which twenty-six writers discuss their dreams, both the sleeping and the waking. There are some remarkably candid remarks from the likes of Maurice Sendak, Amy Tan and Alan Gurganus, who says, "I believe in Whitman's vision that we're all composed of a thousand voices and that those of us who

From *Flowers of Epigrams*
by Timothy Kendal, 1577

My bed, the rest of all my cares,
The end of toiling pain,
Which bringest ease and solace sweet,
While darkness doth remain;
My bed, yield to me slumber sweet,
And trifling dreams repel;
Cause carking care from sobbing breast
To part where it doth dwell;
All mockeries of this wretched world
Put clean from out my mind:
Do these, my bed, and then by thee
Much comfort shall I find.
—Anonymous

have chosen to use our imaginations on a daily basis instead of suppressing our imaginations, which is what the culture frequently demands, are very lucky because we are always in company."

Song on May Morning
by John Milton

Now the bright morning Star, Dayes harbinger,
Comes dancing from the East, and leads with her
The Flowry *May*, who from her green lap throws
The yellow Cowslip and the pale Primrose.
Hail, bounteous *May*, that dost inspire
Mirth and youth and young desire,
Woods and Groves, are of thy dressing,
Hill and Dale doth boast thy blessing.
Thus we salute thee with our early Song,
And welcome thee, and wish thee long.

Hector: May Morning Mist

Altona Winkler, who in addition to writing romance novels sells cosmetic aids door to door, has recently been touting the virtues of a new toner called May Morning Mist. We wonder if the manufacturers of this balm were drawn to the name because of its alliterative appeal, or if they were concerned with preserving a tradition. For centuries, seekers after beauty, and I count myself among them, have believed that the first dews of May were especially beneficial for bleaching out the pores and restoring a youthful lustre to the skin. In *Mother Goose*, we find this advice:

The fair maid who, the first of May,
Goes to the fields at the break of day,
And washes in dew from the hawthorn tree,
Will ever after handsome be.

We suspect that Altona might have had an eager client in Mrs. Pepys, who undertook considerable exertions in the name of complexion enhancement and would certainly have welcomed the convenience of a bottled product. On May 10, 1669, her husband Samuel wrote in his diary:

Troubled about 3 in the morning, with my wife's calling her maid up, and rising herself, to go with her coach abroad to gather May-dew—which she did; and I troubled for it, for fear of any hurt, going abroad so betimes, happening to her. But I to sleep again, and she came home about 6 and to bed again.

Two centuries later, the editors of *Enquire Within Upon Everything* advised their readers that this recipe would free them of the embarrassment of freckles:

Dissolve, in half an ounce of lemon-juice, one ounce of Venice soap, and add a quarter of an ounce each of oil of bitter almonds, and deliquated oil of tartar. Place this mixture in the sun till it acquires the consistency of ointment. When in this state add three drops of the oil of rhodium, and keep it for use. Apply it to the face and hands in the manner following: Wash the parts at night with elder-flower water, then anoint with the ointment. In the morning cleanse the skin from its oily adhesion by washing it copiously in rose-water.

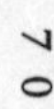

Reading What the Wind Brought: An Auction Catalogue

This leaf from a Sotheby's auction catalogue turned up on our barbed wire. We found it when we went out to weed the lettuce.

Lot 149. Mother's Day cards of historical note. Among the 52 individual items are many fine examples which would be of interest to either a museum or a private collector. Highlights below. For a complete description, with illustrations, see page 112.

1. Card 8. From Oedipus, King of Thebes. Folded papyrus. Faded representation of heart and flowers on outer leaf, believed to be in bull blood. Inside verse, handwritten, reads:

Oh Mother, oh Mother, how well I recall
The summer I met you. Or was it the fall?
I think it was Sunday, the weather was fair,
A rose or gardenia was stuck in your hair.
You whispered come hither, and opened your arms,
You soon made me privy to all of your charms.
Oh Mother, oh Mother, I think it is true,
I'm ever so lucky you told me, "I do!"
I know I'm the envy of all of the guys,
They're jealous enough that they'd gouge out their eyes.
Thanks to you, mama, I'm happy to say,
I never again need to go out to play.

2. Card 14. From Mickey Mouse. On red construction paper. Magazine picture collage decorates front leaf. Inside, calligraphed inscription, black ink, reads:

Dearest Mother, on this day,
This is what I want to say.
Life's been hard for you, I know,
And your row was rough to hoe.
Often you have told me that
Daddy was, in fact, a rat.
And you were, I know, forlorn,
That he left when I was born,
Saying that he could not love
Any son who wore such gloves.
Daddy took the nearest cab,
Signed up at the nearest lab,
Spent his dying ratty days
Chasing cheese around some maze.
As they say, Ma, life's a bitch.
What the hell! At least we're rich.

3. Card 27. From Hamlet, Prince of Denmark. Folded bristol board. Drawing of skull on front leaf, verse inside inscribed in magic marker.

Oh! Gertrude, you're the mother of the looniest of Danes!
I'm moody, slow, and very unreliable.
There's little doubt your little boy is anything but sane,
In fact, I think I'm clearly certifiable.

I bare my bodkin publicly, I find it hard to cope,
I'm stubborn, cold, and anything but pliable.
Oh Mother, you despair about my future, but let's hope
That Hollywood might find my story buyable.

4. Card 36. From Sigmund Freud. Commercial card, sepia-toned illustration of mother standing by child on potty. Lace fringed.

Liebes mutter, what a dame!
You are where I lay the blame
For my every quirk and trauma,
Danke schoen, meine liebes mama!

5. Card 49. Attributed to Bullwinkle. On photocopy paper. Front leaf shows lavender antlers. Typescript inscription reads:

Mama, I've something to tell you,
It won't be too easy to say.
I know I'm a big, virile bull moose,
But nonetheless, Mama, I'm gay.
I know I don't look like a sissy,
I know I don't throw like a girl,
The facts, though, are just as I state them,
And what's more, my boyfriend's a squirrel.
Our path and his name are both Rocky,
Romance between species is hard,
But Mama, oh Mama, I love him!
I'm bringing him home with this card.

Our Guests Write: Jerry

Dear Lads:

Have you noticed how, in recent years, women have restaked their claim to perfectly good words that somewhere along the line slipped from honourable usage? It wasn't so long ago that "spinster" and "crone" cast pejorative shadows: crabbed, dried-out biddies who recycled teabags and kept too many cats; withered hags peering from behind curtains, shaking liver-spotted fists at boys on the street.

Now, the feminist zest for undermining patriarchal certitudes, including those that inform the vernacular, has led to the rehabilitation of these and other words. It's been a long time since anyone suggested seriously that a woman who lives her life without spousal encumbrances has somehow failed to achieve her distaff destiny: so why should "spinster" evoke sympathy or derision? And because the various stigmas attendant on ageing have been exposed and put on trial, "crone" can now be held up as a badge of honour.

I've been thinking about this because I've been reading Gloria Steinem's collection of essays, *Moving Beyond Words.* It contains a piece called "Doing Sixty," in which Ms. Steinem, a no-bullshit spinster, talks about reaching the seventh decade and about her eagerness to embrace what is, in effect, cronedom.

In many respects, Gloria Steinem's gentle geriatric jeremiad is an expanded prose rendering of "Warning," a folksy poem by Jenny Joseph. You've probably seen it reprinted on broadsheets, tea towels and cookie tins. Its famous first line, "When I am an old woman I shall wear purple," is also the title of an anthology of poetry and prose pieces about ageing women.

Gloria Steinem, in a substantial way, and Jenny Joseph, rather more whimsically, suggest a new paradigm of ageing. They encourage women to be stubborn, wilful, tyrannical and lusty as they grow full of days, to seize such epithets as crone and spinster and claim them as their own.

But no one is doing this for men, who, for the most part, are content to worry about their pensions and their prostates and who have shown no interest in rehabilitating such useful words as "grumpy" or "geezer."

Don't you think we are being shortchanged? Don't you think we need a Gloria Steinem equivalent to take over the leadership of an intellectual or societal vanguard? I am not equipped for this, but I'm willing to fill the Jenny Joseph part of the void with this poem, which owes its inspiration entirely to "Warning." Maybe it will serve as kindling for the bigger fire someone braver and smarter than I might one day ignite. I call it "Red Alert."

When I am an old geezer, I shall sleep in the nude,
And loll about on satin sheets till noon,
Just because I like the sound of the word.
I shall annotate my scars for everyone I meet,
And exaggerate the gory bits, especially for children.
And furthermore, I shall have a scooter,
And terrify pedestrians on crowded sidewalks.
I shall fly the skull and crossbones,
And blast Guns N' Roses from my boom box.

Your Love Life in the Stars
by Altona Winkler

TAURUS
April 20 to May 20

Taurus, it's time to take stock! The markets may be bullish, but your love life is showing a bearish aspect just around now. Tread carefully, or the fragile china that is your present relationship will shatter forever! Someone you met on the ferry is thinking inappropriate thoughts about you while in the shower. How does that make you feel?

When I am an old geezer, I shall wear a bad toupee,
And give a dollar to anyone who figures out that it's a joke.
And because I will never have been to war,
I'll talk endlessly about Woodstock,
And the summer of love,
And do my Neil Young impersonation,
Even if no one requests it.
Which they never will.

When I am an old geezer, I shall be grumpy.
Telephone solicitors, door-to-door soul savers,
Wrong-number diallers, customs officers,
Pushy store clerks, dental hygienists,
And anyone who says "Have a nice day"
Will feel the heat of my old-geezer grumpiness.

How grand it will be to at last be free
From mid-life's shackles of polite restraint!
I can't wait for the day to dawn
When I find the old geezer who lurks within.
In just a few days I turn forty.
Do you think that's too soon to begin?

All the best!
Jerry Wiggins,
Lethbridge, Alberta

From Swann
by Carol Shields

Rose is a happy woman; her routines make her happy. When in the early morning she pulls the sheets and blankets smooth and fluffs the pillow on the bed, she feels hopeful about the day ahead. A parade of minor pleasures—like the lucky coin today—reassure her, let her know she's part of the world. And on Friday nights she gets into her pyjamas early and crawls into bed to read. It's only seven-thirty and still fairly light outside. She cleans her face with cold cream and brushes her teeth and creeps under the covers. Her bare feet stretch out contentedly. She might read until midnight or later. Tomorrow is Saturday. She can sleep as late as she likes.

This is the bed her mother and father slept in, though Rose can't recall anything about her father who was a soldier—his mother was a Nadeau, a descendant of Martin Nadeau—who died at Dieppe. It's a comfortable double bed with a walnut-veneer headboard and has a good firm mattress that Rose bought after her mother's last illness and death; and smooth fitted sheets, cotton and Fortrel, a cheerful checked pattern. When Rose reads in bed she props herself up in the middle so that the pillows on each side embrace and warm her.

Only once has she shared this bed with another.

HAIR

Virgil: The Passing Parade

Early in June, J. MacDonald Bellweather II held a lawn sale. Everyone was there, and little wonder. Rarely has the commercial dispersal of one household's dross been so lavishly publicized. Mac plastered lamp standards and community bulletin boards with shocking pink posters reminding the whole of the valley that his fine jetsam was up for tender. He arranged for the door-to-door delivery of flyers detailing the same message. One afternoon, a small plane, trailing a banner with a strange device, buzzed over the island: "COMING SOON! MAC'S YARD SALE!" read the writing in the sky.

Then there was the media campaign. Mac has never been shy about using his position as publisher and editor of *The Occasional Rumour* to promote and advance his own missions and causes. Indeed, fettering, cumbersome journalistic principles such as objectivity and impartiality in no way clog Mac's personal pipeline to public opinion. He won't hesitate to use editorial space to launch a recruiting drive for the Valley Morris Men, or for the Bellweather Lawn Bowling League, or for any of his other pet projects. While the Anglicans rejoice if Mac accords them a minuscule mention of a fowl supper, buried somewhere deep in the classified ads, the sermons he delivers at the Church of God the Technician and Marketer are often reprinted under banner headlines on the paper's front page. In the weeks leading up to his eightieth birthday, Mac used the *Rumour* to let it be known with which mail-order companies he was registered, and which remembrances would please him the most. So, the full-page, full-colour advertisement he ran for his lawn sale was no surprise.

"Don't miss this chance to acquire many fine and rare items at bargain basement prices! Biscuit tins, some inscribed with inspirational verses! Bicycle with carrier basket! An E-Z Boy rocker in attractive plaid! Ashtrays from around the world! A music box that plays the themes from both *Dr. Zhivago* and *Romeo and Juliet!* One chiropractic truss, also useful as a corset! *The Dominion Educator Encyclopaedia*, published in 1910! An authentic gargoyle from Notre Dame Cathedral in Paris!"

I was miffed to see this last item listed. The gargoyle—which was in no way authentic, but merely a plaster replica—had been our eightieth birthday gift to him. "Sale Begins at 11 A.M. Sharp! No Early Birds!" was the stern, bold-faced caveat that ran across the top of the ad.

"Ha!" exclaimed Hector. "We'll see about that!"

There is something about the smell of rummage that rouses the strategizer in my brother. This instinct has possessed him his whole life long. Even as a lad, he would plot for weeks in advance of Halloween, mapping out his trick-or-treat route so that he could maximize his caloric return. He is all the proof I'll ever need that the child is well and truly the father of the man. As the day of the lawn sale drew nigh, I observed the same sharkish twinkle that invades his iris when he finds himself with an impressive collection of Scrabble letters arrayed before him and can whiff his opponent's blood. While it's not an endearing quality, this tendency toward the territorial imperative, I'm persuaded it's genetically programmed. Inevitable. A product of nature rather than nurture. If my twin could be said to have a tragic flaw, it's that there are times in his life when he is too much a slave to his own biology.

So it was that before dawn on the appointed day, when the earliest of the birds was just beginning to twitter, Hector skulked

up the long and winding drive of the Bellweather estate and scaled a handily situated elm. He had chosen his wardrobe carefully for full camouflage effect. His plan was simple: to conceal himself in the tree's verdant crown, from which vantage point he would sneak a covert squinny at the full complement of goods, to memorize the specifics of their placement, then to shinny down the trunk unobserved at the stroke of 11. Replete with this illicit intelligence, he would be perfectly positioned to scoop up as many of the choice bargains as he could carry away. To aid and abet his spying, he was armed with a pair of opera glasses he had purchased through a mail-order catalogue.

Caedmon and I moseyed down to the sale, shortly before noon. A mob scene was unfolding. None of the usual suspects in the madding crowd was behaving in a way that would recommend him or her for eventual inscription on the roster of the earth-inheriting meek. Abel Wackaugh was a blur as he ran from table to table, all speed and determination in spite of the lawn sprinklers and board games and other prizes he clutched to his chest. Rae and June were arguing with an out-of-valley interloper about who would have dominion over some rather tatty looking lawn chairs. Altona was flipping through a huge pile of old magazines, shamelessly removing the perfume strips for her collection. I spied Hector haggling with Mac over the price of some familiar-looking opera glasses.

"Fifty dollars and that price is firm! I won't take a penny less!

"Fifty dollars! That's outrageous! They can't be worth more than thirty brand-new!"

"Nonsense! These glasses have been in the Bellweather family for generations! Fifty dollars is a steal. Come to think of it, I'd better make it sixty!"

I sidled up to my glum twin while he grudgingly peeled four tens and a twenty from his billfold and reclaimed his goods.

"Pray tell?" I inquired, discreetly.

His answer was shaped by the curl of his lip. "I sneezed and dropped the damn things. Before I could get down and grab them, Mac came out and started loading up the tables. He spotted them on the grass, scooped them up and added them to his hoard. I could spit!"

"Look at this!" crowed Abel Wackaugh, elbowing his way through the throng. "What a terrific deal! Three dollars for this thermos, and it's even full of hot coffee!"

I looked from the thermos to Hector and back again. This was no garden variety flask. It was festooned with decals portraying characters from *Pride and Prejudice* and looked remarkably like a thank-you gift we had received from a Jane Austen reading group that had stayed with us once upon a time and guzzled all our port.

"Another casualty of the sneeze?"

Hector looked quite abashed, for the wind had clearly been taken out of his lawn sale sails. And there was worse to come. Just as we were turning our backs on the looting and pillaging and making for home, we heard Mac's loud halloo.

"Ahoy there, you lads! Glad I caught you! I've just realized that it's past time to start planning the Dominion Day parade. Time flies, it surely does! The *Rumour* will be the sponsor, as usual. Means I'll have to be the marshal, I suppose. How many years has it been now? I've lost count. A burden, really. Anyway, I'm on the lookout for a pair of impartial judges for the floats. First prize is $500, all the money I've made at the lawn sale. Have to come up with some consolation awards, too. Maybe that damn

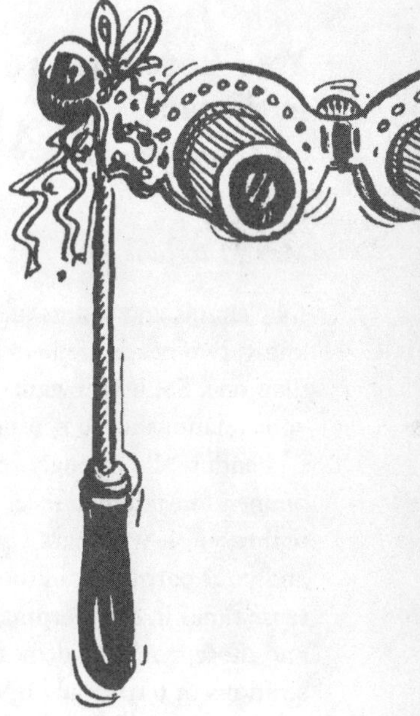

gargoyle, no one bought the thing. Can't say I blame them much. Ugly as sin. So, what do you say? The *Rumour*'s entry is going to be magnificent, the best ever! Say, why not put a float together yourselves? Of course, you won't be able to win, conflict of interest and all. Not that it much matters because, frankly, the *Rumour* will be hard to beat! Impossible, I'd say! Still, winning isn't everything, eh? Spirit of the day and all! That's what counts! The true north strong and free! God save the Queen! Cheers! See you on Dominion Day!"

I forget when Canada Day superseded Dominion Day as the name of our national patriotic observance. Mac is no more willing to accommodate that change than he is ready to embrace the concept of Daylight Saving Time. His clock stays put all the livelong year, which means that during the summer months we have to subtract an hour from any commencement time reported in the *Rumour.*

"His mother must have been frightened by a bulldozer when she was carrying him," said Hector, as we drove home. "And I'd be very curious to learn how he came by his definition of 'conflict of interest.'"

"We *could* say no," I ventured, even though I knew it was a hopeless thought. Saying no to Mac, when yes is the answer he's determined to hear, is about as effective as saying no to a herd of buffalo rampaging towards you. There was nothing for it but to shrug and give in.

And so it was that on July 1, at noon—Mac Standard Time—Hector and I scaled the two stepladders that served as our reviewing stand and prepared to perch in judgement. We'd been given clipboards and sheaves of foolscap for the purpose of note-taking. However, we looked less magisterial than might have been the

Your Love Life in the Stars
by Altona Winkler

GEMINI
May 21 to June 21

As Geminis and sailors all know, two heads are better than one. So, if you want your relationship to prosper and endure, I'd strongly recommend installing a second bathroom. It will spare you and your partner from those tense times in the morning, and those troubling demonstrations of territorial imperative. After all, too many tense mornings gnaw away at love just as surely as waves erode a cliff. So, bite the bullet and call a contractor.

case, as we were wearing broad-brimmed hats and our noses were safeguarded against scorching with an effective but rather loud lime-green zinc cream Altona had thoughtfully provided. We settled ourselves in the blazing sun, gave the signal to begin and watched the parade go by. As always, community participation in the event was very high, which meant that there was hardly anyone left in reserve to serve the useful function of spectator. Nonetheless, the several valley folk and half-dozen of our B&B guests who occupied the sidelines were enthusiastic in their endorsement, clapping and whistling appreciatively.

Mac looked both proud and serene at the head of the parade. He drove his new tractor lawn mower with obvious pride and waved gravely as he led the parade along its prescribed route, which was roughly the quarter mile between the Well of Loneliness and the *Rumour* office. He was followed by the Liver Spots, the marching and twirling rhythm band from the retirement home. They played a bang-up rendition of "When the Saints Go Marching In," which featured some truly remarkable group glockenspiel work. Every so often the band would stop and march in place so that the twirlers could scurry after their batons. "Duck!" they would call each and every time they launched their thin silver satellites.

Behind the Liver Spots strutted the Valley Youth Recorder Ensemble. They proved themselves both agile in dodging the falling batons and musically adept with their version of "The 1812 Overture." The cannon shots were artfully and organically provided by Mandy Henderson, well-known throughout the valley for her ability to belch on demand.

Abel Wackaugh's float was next, an open convertible across the hood of which he had affixed a spray-painted banner that

read: "Wackaugh's Hardware and Hair Styling Emporium." He drove with one hand, and with the other wielded a chainsaw. It was not clear to us which aspect of his two-pronged business he was touting with this prop.

The Valley Morris Men were next, hopping about with a frantic jingling of bells and fevered waving of white hankies. They looked to me as though they were signalling surrender, though to whom they were ceding the battle I couldn't imagine. Just as they were passing by our ladders, a familiar figure leapt into the middle of the fray, thumping and tinkling and calling out "Hoopla! Yoy! Aroint!"

"Isn't that Mac?" I asked, squinting down from on high.

Hector concurred. The marshal had evidently reached the end of the parade route and hustled back in order that he might make a second appearance.

"Behold!" called Hector as Caedmon struggled into view, pulling our own float. He was dressed in a bathrobe and slippers, and waved gamely as he plodded along, harnessed to a surplus bed we'd resurrected from the basement and mounted on casters. It was splendidly draped with a pink and flowing canopy. Altona, alluringly bedecked in what I believe is called a merry widow, or maybe a teddy, was sprawled on the covers, odalisque-style. In order that the concept of breakfast might be added to a tableau in which the idea of bed played so visible a role, she had decided to eat bowlful after bowlful of cold cereal. Every so often, she would reach into one of the several boxes and toss a handful of cornflakes in the general direction of what passed for the crowd.

"Where did she get that outfit?" I asked Hector, who only blushed and cleared his throat by way of reply. "Well of Loneliness entry at 4 o'clock!" he chirped, with the enthusiasm of one who has been saved by the bell. There was Rae, cunningly dressed as a cappuccino, and June as a croissant. Between them they pushed a stroller in which sat their daughter, little Martina.

"What is she supposed to be?" I asked.

Hector raised his opera glasses.

"A demitasse, I believe."

"Of course! And look! Here comes Mac for his third strike!"

With a reindeerlike jangle, and mopping his brow with his hanky, he galloped past and vaulted onto the *Occasional Rumour* float: a grand panorama representative of the history of communication. THE GUTENBERG HOME PAGE: A WHOLE MEDIA EXPERIENCE read the banner that spanned the flatbed truck. With an artfully placed camera translating his every move onto the huge video screen that was part of his setup, and with a dexterity astonishing in a man of his advanced years, Mac donned a Ben Franklin wig, set a couple of lines of type and began to crank out leaflets on an old hand press. He tossed these brochures out to the onlookers. "THE OCCASIONAL RUMOUR! YOUR COMMUNITY NEWSPAPER! GRAND PRIZE WINNER AT THE DOMINION DAY PARADE *FOR TEN CONSECUTIVE YEARS*!" The same message flashed across the video screen, alternating with images of Mac weight lifting, Morris dancing, giving blood and rescuing a kitten from the high branches of a tree.

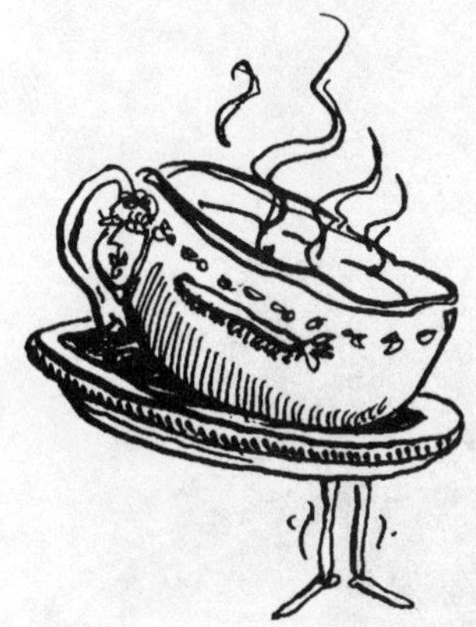

"Do you spell 'overkill' with or without a hyphen?" Hector whispered to me as the float passed on towards the finish line.

Clearly, it had been Mac's intention to be both the alpha and the omega of the Dominion Day Parade. According to our list of official registrants, there were no other floats to come. The display ought properly to have finished with his melding of antique

printing techniques with the pyrotechnics of the latest video technology. But the applause had hardly petered out when there came into view, riding easily in Mac's wake, scudding over the crests of his swells, a late-breaking contrivance that struck both Hector and me as the very definition of the word "float."

"Why, I do believe that's Julia!"

"I do believe you're right," said Hector, surrendering his opera glasses so I might see the better.

Indeed it was. Sweet Julia! She is five, and has been coming to stay at our house since she was *in utero*. When we first met her parents, their only external travelling companion was an English mastiff named Barney. Now they are all four of them welcome visitors and turn up each summer.

Julia rode in state in a little red wagon that was pulled by the slow and decorous dog. She wore a tutu that was a cloudlike mass of tulle. Brown paper wings had been taped to her shoulders. She held a wand—a star covered in foil and mounted on a stick—in her right hand. As she passed along the parade route, she waved it at the watchers and cried in her bright, clear voice: "Poof! You're all happy! Poof! You're all happy!"

And the astonishing thing was that she was right. We were. Her fairy magic worked. There was not a soul at the parade who was not grinning from ear to ear.

With the exception of Mac. There was a certain gritted look to the grand marshal's smile when we announced our unanimous choice of winner. We both thought it peculiar that there was no follow-up story in the *Rumour* and no photograph of the victorious little Julia. It struck us as odd that the $500 prize was somehow mislaid, even though Mac swears it was on the dash of his truck, ready to present to the laureate. One day, perhaps, we will hear the results of the thorough and comprehensive investigation he said he would launch.

Me, I'm not holding my breath. On the contrary, I am taking a page from Barney's book and lying in the shade of the chestnut with my tongue lolling out. The dog days are on us. The weather is pantingly hot. The branches above me are heavy with the nuts that any day now they'll begin to discard. For now they just hang there, waiting for the moment of their ripening. All things in their time. All is as it should be. The magic lingers. We are happy.

How To Behave in a Thunderstorm

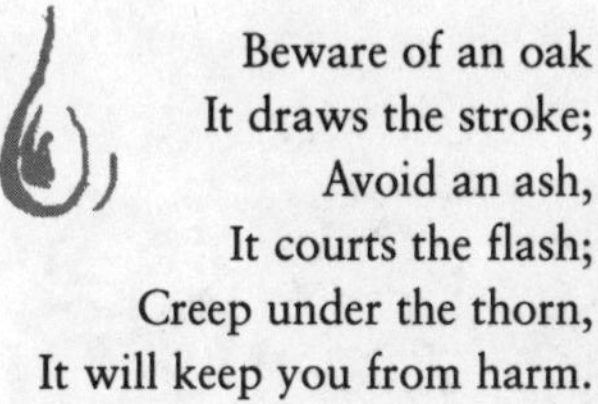

Beware of an oak
It draws the stroke;
Avoid an ash,
It courts the flash;
Creep under the thorn,
It will keep you from harm.

The Artful Picnic
by Mrs. Isabella Beeton

After a cool early summer, it looks as though picnic season is finally upon us. Here then, for the edification of all artful out-of-doors eaters, is Mrs. Isabella Beeton's "Recipe for a Picnic," extracted from the 1861 edition of *Beeton's Book of Household Management:*

Provided care has been taken in choosing congenial guests, and that in a mixed party one sex does not preponderate, a well arranged picnic is one of the pleasantest forms of entertainment.

Watch carefully not to provide too much of one thing and too little of another; avoid serving plenty of salad and no dressing; two or three legs of lamb and no mint sauce; an abundance of wine and no corkscrew; and suchlike little mistakes. Given a happy party of young people bent on enjoyment, these are trifles

light as air, which serve rather to increase the fun than diminish it. But, on the other hand, the party may not be all young and merry; it may be very distasteful to some to have to suffer these inconveniences.

The easiest way to arrange that there should be nothing wanting, is to make out a menu, adding all the little etceteras. It is advisable to estimate quantities extravagantly, for nothing is more annoying than to find everything exhausted and guests hungry. Following is a list of articles that should be provided in addition to the repast:

Wine, bottled beer, soda water, lemonade. Plates, knives, forks, spoons, glasses, tumblers, tablecloths, serviettes, glass cloths, pepper, cayenne, salt, mustard, oil, vinegar, castor sugar, corkscrews, and champagne-opener. A chafing dish and accessories are very useful accompaniments to a picnic.

Recipe for Salad

by the Reverend Sydney Smith (1771-1845)

To make this condiment your poet begs
The pounded yellow of two hard-boil'd eggs;
Two boiled potatoes, passed through kitchen sieve,
Smoothness and softness to the salad give.
Let onion atoms lurk within the bowl,
And, scarce suspected, animate the whole.
Of mordant mustard add a single spoon,
Distrust the condiment that bites so soon;
But deem it not, thou man of herbs, a fault
To add a double quantity of salt.
Four times the spoon with oil from Lucca crown,
And twice with vinegar procured from town;
And, lastly, o'er the flavour'd compound toss
A magic soupçon of anchovy sauce.
Oh, green and glorious! Oh, herbaceous treat!
'Twould tempt the dying anchorite to eat;
Back to the world he'd turn his fleeting soul,
And plunge his fingers in the salad bowl.
Serenely full, the epicure would say,
"Fate cannot harm me, I have dined today!"

Caedmon's Saint of the Month: July

St. Swithun, who was born round about 862, and whose feast day is July 15, was the Bishop and Patron of Winchester. He led a rather dull life, characterized by piety and a measure of political expediency. St. Swithun is perhaps most remarkable for the legend that has grown up around his feast day: that is, if it rains on St. Swithun's Day, it will pour for forty days afterward.

St. Swithun's Day, if thou dost rain,
For forty days it will remain;
St. Swithun's Day, if thou be fair,
For forty days 'twill rain na mair.

This Noah-like prophecy seems to have nothing whatsoever to do with the life and works of the saint, but much to do with the meteorological musings of the straw-chewing rustics of long ago, whose livelihood required they keep a worried eye fixed on the midsummer sky. Let us pray:

St. Swithun, on July 14, we dance a Gallic reel,
We lounge about and close our eyes and think of the Bastille,
And offer up a prayer to you, and keep our pleading plain:
Please ensure that on your day we won't have any rain.
We would not have our summer ruined by forty soggy days!
For what about our picnics, and our tennis and croquet?
And what about the sunscreen we're all eager to apply?
Prithee then, St. Swithun, won't you keep your feast day dry?

Your Love Life in the Stars

by Altona Winkler

CANCER
June 22 to July 22

Oddly enough, Cancer, it looks to me as though your Wednesday nights are full of promise for this coming quarter. However, I can't tell if that's because of your romantic prospects or because of the dynamite TV line-up for the season. Either way, your mid-week is going to be a heck of a lot of fun! But as for the weekend, I'd find a good video store.

Reading What the Wind Brought: A Workshop Brochure

POET BUSTER
Are Your Employees
Writing Poetry at Work?

You're an administrative assistant or supervisor or personnel officer. You till the fertile fields of middle management. Day after day, you are called upon to be vigilant, to make sure that the sheep in your fold don't sacrifice their work time on the pilfering altar of such activities as hanging around the water cooler, gossiping on the phone, necking in the supply room, shooting up in the washroom or E-mailing friends in Milano. But are you aware of a recent Bureau of Work Measurement study which proves conclusively that hundreds of thousands of dollars in potential revenue are lost each year to the wilfulness of employees who write poetry at work? The cost of subversive versifying greatly exceeds those incurred by such widespread petty office crimes as paper clip thievery, or rubber band shooting contests, or the pirating of photocopiers and fax machines to first duplicate, and then disseminate, vile images of bare bottoms.

This five-day workshop will teach you how to look for the warning signs that poetry is afoot; how to take pre-emptive measures to forestall the writing of poetry in the work environment; and how to deal with the problem effectively and humanely once the poets have been found out. Here is a day-by-day breakdown of the workshop.

DAY ONE

Embracing the concept that forewarned is forearmed, and understanding that an enemy can only be defeated when you can read his heart, you will undergo a closely supervised immersion into the awful, addictive world of poetry. Such seductive concepts as rhythm, rhyme, ballads, dactyls, caesuras, consonance, scansion, hypermetrical syllables, front vowels, mosaic rhyme, fricatives, hexameter and hendecasyllablic lines will be introduced in the morning.

The afternoon will consist of a comprehensive survey of world poetry, from Beowulf to the present day. You will also be expected to write a sestina, a Petrarchan sonnet and a haiku. There is no need to fret about getting "hooked" through this exposure. Our facilitators are all trained in emergency procedures, and detoxifying spreadsheets will be made available to all attendees before they are sent home.

DAY TWO

The second day of the workshop will place the problem of poetry in its historical context. You will learn that Chaucer, Shakespeare, Donne, both the Brownings, Walt Whitman, Wallace Stevens and Stevie Smith all cost their employers millions upon millions of dollars. There will be a detailed examination of their undercutting ways, and a case-by-case study of the invidious means by which they were able to bilk their companies for millions of dollars over their respective tenures.

DAY THREE

You will learn how to spot the telltale, warning signs of poetry early on.

Do your workers arrive late, with black circles under their eyes, and a rhyming dictionary in hand?

Do they lard their conversation with references to Keats, Shelley, Tennyson or Plath? Do they show sudden and marked tendencies to lapse into simile or metaphor, such as "The stapler is a laconic machine gun." "Look, Mr. Jones! With antlike perseverance, the photocopier is marching toward the hundredth copy!"

Do they habitually return late from coffee breaks, looking flushed and dazed in ways no mere caffeine fix can induce, and with inkstains on their fingers?

Do they lapse into iambs of blank verse in the middle of important sales meetings?

You will see by looking at my flip chart
And other audio-visual aids
That the campaign we have been devising
Will certainly enhance your market share.

Or worse, do they inadvertently speak in rhyme? You've got trouble if a simple question like "How are things in the steno pool, Miss Smith?" garners this response:

The only thing this office lacks
Is proper paper for the fax.
Otherwise, we're very merry,
Each and every secretary.

DAY FOUR

Now that you appreciate the enormity of the problem, you will learn ways and strategies that really work to enforce the "No Poetry at Work" rule. These include the following:

How to establish a snitch line so that workers can rat on colleagues whom they suspect of poem-making in the workplace.

How to implement year-end bonuses for those who can demonstrate convincingly that they haven't scribbled a single trochee or spondee. How to make attractive posters advising of the fiscal and psychic dangers of writing poetry between 9 and 5, Monday to Friday.

How to administer a public flogging.

DAY FIVE

We end on a humane and cheerful note, with a day-long session on "Loving the Sinner and Hating the Sin." A discussion of effective intervention strategies with executives from anti-poetry firms will be followed by testimonials from employees who have successfully completed rehabilitation programmes and now actively campaign against poetry in the office and factory.

Early registration is recommended. The number of participants is limited, and recent Poet Buster sessions in Los Angeles, New York and Toronto have sold out within days of being made available to professionals like you. Send your cheque for $1500 (add $20 per day if bag lunch is required). Do it now, 'cause poems are bad. Send your cash! We'll all be glad.

May We Recommend: The Bachelor Brothers' List of Poets and Anthologies for People Who Hate Poetry

How does it happen that so many people who are devoted readers of fiction or biography or essays wrinkle their noses at the mention of poetry? How has it happened that poetry, which is nothing if not a natural and gut-driven response to experience, has come to be regarded as difficult and impenetrable? We can only suppose it has to do with something that happens in school, that the chosen texts, or the ways in which we are taught to read them, sap poetry of its magic: which is, we think, a key word here. The best poetry *is* magic. It should serve as a spell, an incantation, should bring about transformation and psychic shape-shifting. It sounds rather grand to say so, but we think that a society that is wholly cut off from poetry—and ours runs that risk—is a society that has lost any sense of connectedness with its own heartbeat. These poets and anthologies of poems are a kind of prescription to overcome the fear of poetry; to usher a willing reader into a wider world of image and wonder and song from which it is a pity to be an unnecessary exile.

archy & mehitabel by Don Marquis. A minor classic, and the only piece of writing we can think of that can impute qualities of charm to a cockroach. Heaven knows, Kafka didn't manage it. archy is the roach in question, the corporeal home to a soul that once belonged to a *vers libre* poet. archy commandeers Marquis's typewriter at night and leaps from key to key, bashing them down with a tremendous effort. Capital letters are beyond his control and punctuation is out of the question, so the final product has a

kind of e. e. cummings cast to it. archy reveals what the world looks like to one of the roachy persuasion and also interprets the life and times, present and past, of a cat called mehitabel. She is no stranger to the transmigration of souls. Once, she was Cleopatra. She accepts her feline assignment with equanimity and a "wotthehell" nonchalance. "toujours gai, kid, toujours gai" is her motto and constant refrain.

Collected Poems by Charlotte Mew. Charlotte Mew, who was tiny and eccentric and given to manly garb, and who lived with her sister and a vicious parrot called Willie, and whose output was small but sufficiently brilliant to gain her the admiration of Thomas Hardy and Virginia Woolf, and who killed herself by drinking Lysol, was summed up in one newspaper obituary with the damning phrase "said to be a writer." Her preoccupation with religion and the supernatural world comes through in her oddly cadenced, compelling poems, which are like sad and sophisticated nursery rhymes. Latterly, there has been a rekindling of interest in her life and writing, thanks in large measure to a fine critical biography by Penelope Fitzgerald called *Charlotte Mew and Her Friends*.

Come Hither compiled by Walter De la Mare. We admire De la Mare both as a poet and a novelist, but it was as an anthologist that his genius at making connections found its finest expression. This collection of "rhymes and poems for the young of all ages" is, to our way of thinking, one of three or four compendia that can be truly called "indispensable." The selections are so wide-ranging and so cunningly arranged—from Elizabeth I to Robert Frost, from Elinor Wylie to Eleanor Farjeon—and the notes so intriguing and inclined to wander that you can't help but get caught up in this web of words. Much the same can be said

Your Love Life in the Stars
by Altona Winkler

LEO
July 23 to August 22

Proud, sad Leo! I want you to think about this seriously. What's easier? Confining your dating activity to dimly lit bistros—or buying some really terrific skin cream to make those deep wrinkles a thing of the past? Here's a hint to those of you who like a natural skin conditioner. You will feel tremendously refreshed if you lie down for fifteen minutes with sliced strawberries on your face. It's amazing! Afterward, you're perfectly poised to make a tasty shortcake, too! Try it. You won't be disappointed.

of his anthology about sleep, *Behold, This Dreamer!* We are now working on our second copy, having worn out the first. Dropping it in the bath didn't help.

Mother Goose. It is a tragedy of adult life that we consign *Mother Goose* to the nursery.

Bat, bat, come under my hat,
And I'll give you a slice of bacon;
And when I bake, I'll give you a cake,
If I am not mistaken.

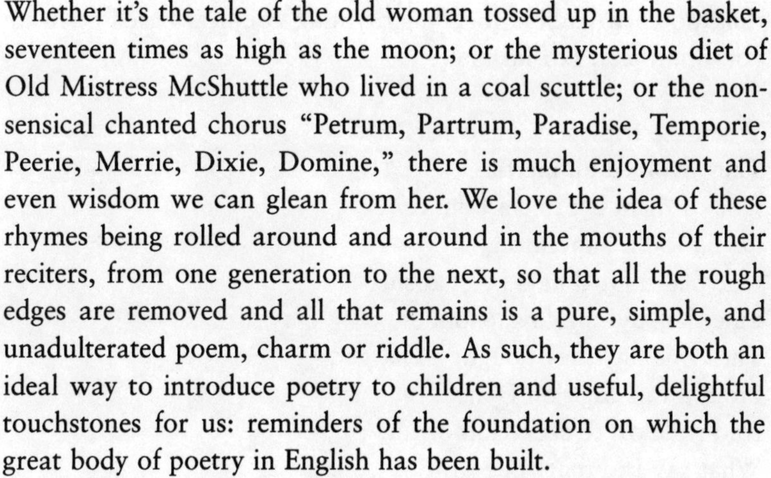

Whether it's the tale of the old woman tossed up in the basket, seventeen times as high as the moon; or the mysterious diet of Old Mistress McShuttle who lived in a coal scuttle; or the nonsensical chanted chorus "Petrum, Partrum, Paradise, Temporie, Peerie, Merrie, Dixie, Domine," there is much enjoyment and even wisdom we can glean from her. We love the idea of these rhymes being rolled around and around in the mouths of their reciters, from one generation to the next, so that all the rough edges are removed and all that remains is a pure, simple, and unadulterated poem, charm or riddle. As such, they are both an ideal way to introduce poetry to children and useful, delightful touchstones for us: reminders of the foundation on which the great body of poetry in English has been built.

New and Selected Poems by Mary Oliver. An American poet whose simple, soulful, finely crafted work is almost wholly devoid of any direct reference to people, and whose poems are among the most intimate and telling we've ever read. Mary Oliver's principal subject is nature, and her acute observations of starfish, grasshoppers, herons and lilies convey the distinct feeling of eavesdropping on someone having a private conversation with God. This is a book for beside the bed. When you wake at 3 A.M. with a rootless sense of dread, it always gives comfort.

The Penguin Rhyming Dictionary. Or any other rhyming dictionary will do. This is an aberrant entry on this list, in that it is neither the work of a single poet nor an anthology. We include it here because one of the best ways of appreciating poetry is to try one's hand at writing it. There is no better way to get the ball rolling than to spend a few instructive minutes thumbing through a rhyming dictionary (cachinnate, machinate, echinate, pollinate, declinate, reclinate, culminate, fulminate, supinate) before settling down to cobble together rhyming couplets based on what you find there. For instance:

When the triplets went to Persia,
They avoided all inertia:
One of them became a bouncer,
One a radio announcer,
One determined he'd keep kosher
Like they did in Nova Scotia.
Then one day they bought a charger,
From a raja high on Djaja,
And rode off to seek Gomorrah.
What say I to that? Begorra!

You see what is possible with just a little application? And to think that some people waste their time with such fripperies as bridge.

The Rattle Bag edited by Seamus Heaney and Ted Hughes. Like *Come Hither,* this book was designed with young readers in mind, but it belongs on the bookshelf of everyone who likes, or who would like to like, poetry. Two very fine poets are the compilers, and they have drawn from a very deep well: Ogden Nash, Walt Whitman, Emily Dickinson, Sylvia Plath, Robert Graves, Elizabeth Bishop are all here, as are numbers of poems in translation, including some thrilling hunting songs of the Yoruba. The poems are arranged alphabetically by title, which lends an air of randomness and surprise to the anthology.

Selected Poems by Stevie Smith. An engaging mix of wistful melancholy, jagged humour and spiritual longing inhabits these offbeat and deceptively simple poems by an English spinster who went to stay with her aunt when she was three and lived the whole of her life in that house in Palmers Green. Perhaps her geographic stability and disinclination to marry are two of the reasons we're so drawn to her. She decorated her books with drawings that are reminiscent of Edward Lear, another poet to whom poetry-resistant readers might turn.

The Stuffed Owl: An Anthology of Bad Verse by D. B. Wyndham Lewis and Charles Lee.

Ye monsters of the bubbling deep,
Your Maker's praises shout,
Up from the sand, ye codlings, leap
And wag your tails about.

That memorable quatrain, from "a Boston hymnodist unknown," is typical of the poetry contained in this wry little anthology, which was first published in 1930 and which holds up for ridicule such dead and defenceless unfortunates as Alfred Austin for his line "He fell upon his hands in the warm, wet slop." Not all the poets are anonymous or obscure. Mrs. Browning is skewered for

"Will you oftly murmur softly?" and Wordsworth, Poe, Tennyson, Keats, Byron and Longfellow all take a drubbing. Each poet's folly is underscored by a truly wicked introduction. This is a good book to have on hand as an illustration of how even the Greats had their off-days.

With Great Pleasure: An Anthology of Poetry and Prose from the BBC Radio 4 Programme edited by Alec Reid. On the popular and long-running BBC programme *Desert Island Discs,* writers, actors, artists, politicians, scientists and other prominent people in public life have the chance to concoct a self-portrait by choosing music and explaining its importance in their lives. *With Great Pleasure* is founded on the same principle, except that the guests select poems (often venerable chestnuts) and prose passages, rather than telling tunes. It's a very revelatory exercise that gives the listener (or reader, in this case) a particular glimpse into the predilections and turns of mind of the participants. For instance, when you know Jacqueline DuPré's story of the importance of the John Masefield poem "Cargoes" to her early childhood, or when you read of her fondness for nature, expressed through her selection of the D. H. Lawrence poem "Hummingbird," you might listen differently to the way she plays a Bach cello suite. Virgil felt a particular fondness for and even kinship with Diana Rigg, when he noted that among her choices was Walter De la Mare's magical "The Listeners," which is one of his favourite poems. Sometimes, if you have been courting sleep and counting sheep for a long time to no good effect, it helps to imagine what you might choose if you were to appear on *With Great Pleasure*. Not only is it a sure soporific, it leads to pleasant dreams.

Friday night's dream,
on Saturday told,
Is sure to come true,
be it never so old.

Dreams of Flying
by Leigh Hunt

Nothing is more common, or usually more pleasant, than to dream of flying. It is one of the best specimens of the race; for besides being agreeable, it is made up of the dreams of ordinary life and those of surprising combination. Thus the dreamer sometimes thinks he is flying in unknown regions, sometimes skimming only a few inches above the ground, and wondering he never did it before. He will even dream that he is dreaming about it; and yet is so fully convinced of its feasibility, and so astonished at his never having hit upon so delightful a truism, that he is resolved to practise it the moment he wakes. "One has only," says he, "to give a little spring with one's foot, so and—oh! it's the easiest and most obvious thing in the world. I'll always skim hereafter." We dreamt once that a woman set up some Flying Rooms, as a person does a tavern. We went to try them, and nothing could be more satisfactory and commonplace on all sides. The landlady welcomed us with a courtesy, hoped for friends and favours, etc., and then showed us into a spacious room, not round, as might be expected, but long, and after the usual dining fashion. "Perhaps, sir," said she, "you would like to try the room." Upon which we made no more ado, but sprung up and made two or three genteel circuits, now taking the height of it, like a house-lark, and then cutting the angles, like a swallow. "Very pretty flying indeed," said we, "and very moderate."

The Vacuum Cleaner Dream
by Gwendolyn MacEwen

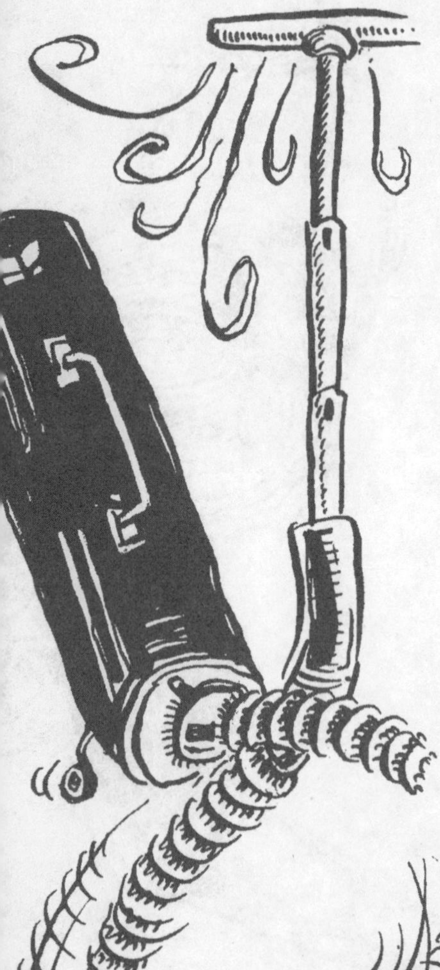

I dreamt I was vacuuming the universe
and everything got sucked
into my blind machine
whirr whirr whirr

I was an avenging angel
and the best cleaning woman in the world.

I dreamt I was vacuuming
with a sickening efficiency
and everything went into
the head of the extra-galactic vacuum beast,
expertly tamed by me,
avenging angel
and the best cleaning woman
in the world.

And when I opened the bag
to empty it I found:
a dictionary of dead tongues
a bottle of wine
lunar dust
the rings of Saturn
and the sleeping body of my love.

From *The Moon by Whale Light*
by Diane Ackerman

When a whale sleeps, it slowly tumbles in an any-old-crazy, end-over-end, sideways fashion, and may even bonk its head on the bottom. Or it just lies quietly, looking like a corpse. When it rises again to breathe in the midst of its sleep, it comes up as slow as a dream, breaks the surface, breathes a few times and, without even diving, falls again slowly toward the bottom. Right whales sometimes sleep in the mornings on calm days in Argentina, and some of them seem to be head-heavy, with light tails. The result is that they fall forward and their tails rise out of the water. Humpbacks are rarely visible when they're sleeping, because they're less buoyant and usually sink fast. But the behavior of right whales is easy to study, because they're at least surface whales. They're so fat that they float when relaxed, and they spend a lot of time with their backs in the air. When they're asleep at the surface, their breathing rate drops tremendously, they don't close their nostrils completely between breaths, and so sometimes they snore. In fact, they make marvellous, rude, after-dinner noises as they sleep. When they wake, they stretch their backs, open their mouths, and yawn. Sometimes, they lift their tails up and shake them, and they go about their business. Often, they sleep at the surface so long on calm days their backs get sunburned; and then they peel the same way humans do, but on a big, and whale-size scale. The loose skin from their backs falls into the water and becomes food for the birds. When they breach, they shed a lot of loose skin as they hit the water, and seagulls, realizing this, fly out fast to a breaching whale. Not much skin sheds from the tail. The gulls know that, and when a whale is merely hitting its tail on the water, they don't bother with it.

The Properties of a Good Greyhound

by Dame Julia Berners, 1388

A greyhound should be headed like a Snake,
And necked like a Drake,
Footed like a Cat,
Tailed like a Rat,
Sided like a Team,
Chined like a Beam.

The first year he must learn to feed,
The second year to field him lead,
The third year he is fellow-like,
The fourth year there is none sike,
The fifth year he is good enough,
The sixth year he shall hold the plough,
The seventh year he will avail
Great bitches for to assail,
The eighth year lick ladle,
The ninth year to cart saddle,
And when he is commen to that year
Have him to the tanner,
For the best hound that ever bitch had
At nine year he is full bad.

Our Guests Write: Linda

Hello to all at the BBB&B! Are you up to your hips in end-of-summer chores? Lots of canning and jam-making going on? Back east, our long Indian summer has finally started to fizzle. After one or two false starts and a few fitful episodes of unaccountable stage fright, autumn is again mincing down the runway, sporting her coat of many colours. One look stirs the hopeless nostalgia, the achy longings that this season alone can rekindle.

Whence come these autumnal impulses? I cannot say. I only know that once the wishbone is hung to dry and the rains of October commence, all manner of uncommon hungers rise to the fore. I want to lay in a cord or two of wood even though I wouldn't know a cord if I woke up in one. I want to undertake long and tedious procedures in order to produce dubious versions of domestic supplies cheaply and readily available at the store a block away. I want to render fat to soap. Grind my own flour. Knit up a couple of mufflers. Make candles out of tallow, whatever that may be.

In every instance, these base instincts have been squashed under the overbearing but sensible governance of intellect. However, it is proving far more difficult to forestall a rather more grim urge: to considerably cull the local squirrel population, by violent means if necessary.

Why should I find myself inhabited by such a gruesome need? I can't explain it. Such murderous musings really aren't in keeping with my live and let live, civil libertarian character. I don't know what it is about squirrels at this time of year that makes me want to pick up my thesaurus and contemplate the listings under

"decimate." Others to whom I've spoken can much more easily validate a lust for squirrel blood than can I. I have never had them invade my attic, or chew through wiring, or keep me awake at night with their intramural scurrying. My response is purely intuitive. There's just something about them that seems to me to embody evil. Maybe it's because of their oppressive omnipresence, their random skitterings, their frivolous disregard for the rules of the road and traffic patterns, the way they engineer an explosion of chestnuts when I'm passing beneath a tree. Or it could just be that I am a conduit for the pent-up bitterness of my dog Cinders.

When the wind
is in the east,
'Tis neither good
for man nor beast.
When the wind
is in the north,
The skilful fisher
goes not forth.
When the wind
is in the south,
It blows the bait
in the fishes' mouth.
When the wind
is in the west,
Then 'tis at the very best.
—Anonymous

Poor Cinders! It's not her fault her environs are so unremittingly urban that she can't leave the house unless she is on a leash. Nor is she responsible for the fact that the part of her brain that might grasp the concept of what a leash is and does atrophied a long time ago. She is not to blame for the genetic mix that makes her see a squirrel as something like a hirsute cookie on four legs, a prize to be sought after at any cost. She can hardly be slighted just because every time she sees or scents a squirrel—and this happens about fifty-seven times a day at this time of year—she tenses, points, lunges and is pulled up short, half a league from her would-be prey. She is indefatigably stupid about this. She does it time and time again, with all the awful, dumb persistence of Sisyphus.

Cinders is a fat dog. No one seeing her in action would believe her capable of the rigours of hunting. Passers-by snicker meanly at the sight of the barrel-shaped mutt making attempt after aborted attempt to bag one of the glorified rats that plague her days. The squirrels themselves look on her efforts with bland nonchalance that cuts us both to the quick. Derisive snickers from pedestrians, vain chatterings from squirrels: we've grown accustomed to them. But one day, we'll surprise them all. One day, the impeding leash will slip from my hand, and the dog will show the lightning quick stuff of which I know her to be made. There'll be a swift collision of instinct, paw and jaw, and it will be game over for some pea-brained nut gatherer. The neighbours will be shocked into silence. Every squirrel in the vicinity will stop in its tracks and quake before taking to the trees and opting for early hibernation.

These are the comforting reassurances I try to whisper to Cinders to assuage the sting of defeat. But before I'm halfway through, she's once again mapping out her doomed strategy. She's creeping through the leaves, fully 10 metres away from her intended prey and only centimetres from frustration. She's full of admirable purposefulness. She's oblivious to the loveliness of the world that is changing all around us. Of course she is! Because maybe, just maybe, this will be the one.

Good wishes to you all!

Linda Herman, Dartmouth, Nova Scotia

When the weather is wet,
We must not fret:
When the weather is dry,
We must not cry:
When the weather is cold,
We must not scold:
When the weather is warm,
We must not storm:
But be thankful together,
Whatever the weather.
—Anonymous

Ten Canine Seminal Myths and Articles of Faith

And speaking of dogs and their ways, here is the text of a faded newspaper clipping that our friends Rae and June have attached to their fridge. They keep it there in honour of their dog, Toklas.

1. Genesis

In the beginning, there was Mitzi. And Mitzi made the heavens and the earth and divided light from dark, made the land and the sky and the sea, and all the furred and feathered and finned denizens that walk, fly, and swim thereupon and therein and therethrough. And all this Mitzi did on six busy days. And on the seventh day, Mitzi wanted company. And so she made the first biped, Gary. And Gary wanted very much to rest. But Mitzi would not deign to have him lie prostrate before the idol of idle Sundays. And so she invented the beach and then the Frisbee. And she spent the whole of the Sabbath teaching the biped Gary how these agents could coalesce. And she called it Paradise, for she saw that it was good.

2. The Sniffing of Butts and the Licking of Privates

In the beginning there was Mitzi, and then there was Gary. But Mitzi needed a companion who was her equal both in mind and leg. For Gary, as it turned out, had his limits, although his opposable thumbs proved useful for the opening of tins, and so he wasn't a complete waste of clay. And so she took up a spare bone, only slightly gnawed, and made herself Jake. And Jake she made in her own image. So successful was she in this mission that she was unable to tell Jake from herself, which led to all manner of

Your Love Life in the Stars

by Altona Winkler

VIRGO

August 23 to September 22

Darling Virgo! Your high school sweetheart is going to get in touch! The pity is that after twenty-five years he's still in high school, and the only reason he's calling is that he thinks you can help him with his algebra. I know this all sounds terribly cruel, but remember that the stars are wholly impartial and never, ever lie. Don't despair. It's possible that romance will pick up soon.

existential quandaries and confusion around the supper dish. Happily, she learned soon enough that there was a foolproof way to distinguish between them. This was that Mitzi tasted like Mitzi, and Jake smelled like Jake. And so it was that, to circumvent mixups, she began the regime dogs practise to this day, as recorded in the proverb:

If you're not sure that you are you, recall this simple trick:
Lie down in the living room and give yourself a lick.
And when you meet another dog, remember how to tell
That dog is not in fact yourself: just give his butt a smell.

3. **Paradise Lost**

And the day came that Gary got just a little too big for his breeches. For Mitzi would ask nicely for some pot roast, and Gary would say "Bad dog!" And Mitzi would sleep on the couch, and Gary would say "Bad dog!" And Mitzi would pick up the Frisbee, and Gary would say, "Not now!" And Mitzi one day said, "Just who the hell is the alpha pooch around here anyway?" And she said, "Okay, Gary. You've had your chance. I've had enough. Thus shall it be with you and with all your children's children. Ye shall become gatherers of droppings, and these ye shall pick up in bags from the supermarket, and so it shall be from this day forward, throughout all of time. And ye shall bend down and ye shall scoop and ye shall say, "Yeeeeeee!" And what's more, ye shall have licensing bylaws, and leashing regulations, and every time ye walk into a veterinarian's office ye shall be compelled to write a cheque for no less than a hundred bucks. And see how ye like them apples." And it was so.

4. Why Dogs Like to Roll in Dead Marine Life
And it came to pass that Mitzi one day bade representatives from a wide demographic swath throughout her creation to come bow before her and pay their taxes. And so they journeyed, one after the other, the skunk and the butterfly and the badger and the moose, each one intent on rendering unto Mitzi. And the fish came too, gasping the burning oxygen from out of the dangerous air. And when the fish stood before the throne of Mitzi, he breathed his last and collapsed before her. And Mitzi was moved by this, and honoured the fish by declaring that his death would not be in vain; that henceforward, all dogs would honour all dead fish by rolling in them, over and over. And Mitzi sealed her promise by being the first to apply this pungent cologne.

5. Why Bipeds Twitch in Their Sleep
They are chasing after faster cars and bigger pay cheques.

6. Why Bipeds Have Two Legs
Variety is the spice of life, and it would simply be too boring if they had only one limb that was readily accessible for dogs to hump.

7. The Length of Biped Lives in Real Years
On average, a North American or European biped can count on living 525 years. This is another aspect of the curse of Mitzi, given that only the most charitable or blinkered of creatures would be able to look at the way bipeds work for all their days, and conjure up the verb "to live."

8. What Bipeds See When They Watch Television
Exactly what they see when they look inside the supermarket bags they take along on dog walks.

9. Why Dogs Have Tails
Where else would they hang their feathers?

10. The Greatest of All the Truths
Life *is* a bitch, and dog spelled backward is still dog.

From *The Diary of Samuel Pepys*

"September 11, 1661.
To Dr. Williams, who did carry me into his garden, where he hath abundance of grapes. And did show me how a dog that he hath doth kill all the Cattes that come thither to kill his pigeons, and doth afterwards bury them. And doth it with so much care that they shall be quite covered, that if but the tip of the tail hangs out, he will take up the cat again and dig the hole deeper—which is very strange. And he tells me he doth believe that he hath killed above 100 cats."

Hector: In Came the Lady with the Alligator Purse

Ever since our zygote days, Virgil and I have lived in each other's pockets and made free with each other's coins. After all these years of close and daily contact, I can safely say I know him as well as I know myself. But no one should suppose that we own the same mind or that when one of us speaks it might just as well be the other throwing his voice. No, indeed! If you were to ask us to complete one of those magazine surveys ("Are You a Happy Person?" "Are You a Considerate Lover?" "What's Your Recycling IQ?"), you would see how divergent we are in our tastes and views. But at the same time, we could either of us tell you quite handily how the other brother had answered every question, and where he had placed his defining mark. If Virgil's mazy thinking were a path, I could walk its twists and turns blindfolded and always know precisely where I was. And he would say the same of me.

Diversity of opinion does not necessarily suggest incompatibility. Perhaps one of the reasons we have endured so long under one roof is that along our linked but separate ways we have independently reached the same—or at least similar—conclusions about a sufficient number of life's thorny and divisive issues. For instance, we are neither of us inclined to buy any food product tainted with the modifier "lite." We are both scrupulous about cleaning the lint trap. Neither of us cares about keeping books on the shelf in alphabetical order. And neither of us has ever regretted opening our private home to public scrutiny by undertaking this bed and breakfast experiment.

We knew at the outset of the operation that our lives would shed their old familiar skins, but we have been able to adapt to the necessary changes with equanimity. After all, it wasn't as though we were given to elaborate Wiccan rituals that required the sacrifice of small animals. It wasn't as though we were wedded to the idea of at-home nudism. I was glad enough to give up cigarettes in order to accommodate our "thank you for not smoking" policy. If I am less inclined to leave coffee grounds in the sink, or if I am more punishing of cobwebs than was once the case—so much the better! My one small regret is that I have had to set aside my afternoon lie-downs on the couch in the library.

Perhaps even this abandonment, which I made in the name of decorum, was unnecessary. We try to make company feel at home by treating them in a cordial, inclusive, one-of-the-family kind of way. We have never aspired to blamelessness, never tried to hide our each and every wart. At the same time, there are standards and expectations that must be met. It would scarcely be seemly for our visitors to stumble across one of their two hosts splayed out on the sofa, hogging the whole of its plush expanse, dead to the world and/or drooling. I could quite understand how a paying guest might feel in some way let down by this, might feel that the guardian of the castle was remiss in his vigilance. A slipshod sentry.

I'm sorry this is the case, for I have always liked to nap. I am good at it. In fact, it is one of the few arts at which I am preternaturally gifted and about which I have developed a comprehensive philosophy. To begin with, let it be said that a proper nap cannot be had in bed. Bed suggests commitment, a real marriage to sleep. A nap is a dalliance, a brief affair, a little fling. It is a chance and fleeting meeting, intense, that should be quickly and thoughtlessly consummated as soon as the urge takes hold. There is no refusing a nap once it has insinuated its way into your thoughts. It will take you on the spot. There is no point in whimpering "no, no" in its ear; no point in being coy. A nap knows that you want it as much as it wants you. The best you can do is hope that it will be gentle and won't overstay its welcome.

I feel sorry for people who say they are incapable of napping, or who wake from a siesta feeling cranky and out-of-sorts, annoyed at themselves for giving in to an impulse which they think is a sign of childishness or laxity. I can think of nothing so agreeable as coming to the surface after twenty minutes lost in Napland, settling slowly back into wakefulness, noting the new slant of the sun across the room, amazed to see that he is that much farther along in his diary jottings.

And now it is November: a season of waning light, rich in poignancy, when all our hibernating instincts come to the fore. Oh, it's prime time for us diurnal snoozers! And oh, how happy I was when I settled in for a short, prewinter nap just the other afternoon! All the indicators were right for a truly memorable kip. For one thing, I was completely tuckered out from the exertions of the morning, having spent long hours helping our local Boy Scout and Girl Guide troops tidy up the cemetery. For years now, this has been their annual All Souls' Day community project. It's a good time for such an undertaking, coming as it does before Remembrance Day, when there are wreath-laying ceremonies for which the dead should look their best; and after Halloween, when the bawdy spiritualists who congregate among the stones leave behind beer cans, cigarette butts, and even more tawdry signs of revelry. Almost everyone in the valley who is in any way able-bodied turns out for this event. We meet to gather

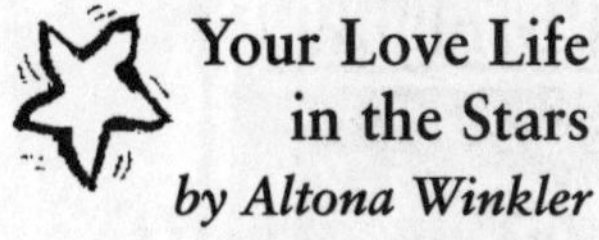

Your Love Life in the Stars

by Altona Winkler

LIBRA

September 23 to October 23

Trips to the recycling centre are a terrific way to meet other well-balanced and environmentally aware individuals. If you see someone who looks a likely playmate, volunteer to help him or her strip off labels. You can learn a lot about a person by studying his or her bottles and tins. Good signs: champagne and caviar receptacles. Bad signs: no-name pop bottles and bean cans.

up litter, to gossip about the living and the long absent, to place flowers and pull weeds, and to tend to some of the more neglected headstones: scraping away the obliterating moss, setting upright any markers that wind or vandals might have uprooted. It's good for the children, too. It connects them to this place. They are able to hear stories of the long-departed from the community elders. And they are able to take in the salutary reminder that this is what all life comes to, in the end.

When everything was shipshape in the graveyard, we all scattered off in our various directions on our various missions. Altona had to hurry off to cover a story for the *Rumour*.

"I'll drop by later on tonight," she trilled as she jumped into her car.

Virgil was heading down to the Well of Loneliness for a pick-me-up cappuccino and a visit with Rae and June.

"Come along," he said, "you look like you could use a caffeinated shot in the arm just now."

"No, no," I demurred, "I have some things to do back home."

I was imagining just how it would be. Our guests had checked out that morning. None were scheduled to arrive till the next day. This meant that not only would I be able to nap, I would be able to revisit my old dozing grounds on the library couch. Hallelujah!

At home, I savoured the silence of the house. There was only the tocking of the mantel clock and the occasional hum of the fridge. Waffle was nowhere to be seen. Mrs. Rochester was staring inscrutably into the middle distance, possibly remembering some long-ago, rain-forest adventure from her tropical past. I washed off the worst of the cemetery, extinguished the ringer on the phone, stretched out prone on the couch, and was gone within seconds, like Alice tumbling down the rabbit hole. I must have been fifteen minutes into the vertiginous spiral when I was wakened by the bracking of the doorbell. I stumbled to answer it. Imagine my bleary eyed surprise to find Her Majesty the Queen on the porch.

In fact, this is an eventuality for which I was somewhat prepared. For years now, I have carried two set pieces in my head. One is my Academy Award acceptance speech. This is among my favourite bathtub fantasies. I can see it all so clearly—the opening of the envelope, then the loaded, magic words: "And the winner is—HECTOR!" For what am I being rewarded? Acting? Directing? Costume design? Special effects? How the hell should I know? I have never been near a film set in my life! It doesn't matter in the slightest. The scene always plays out in the same way. A look of shock, delight, and disbelief comes over my face. I rise, bend to kiss Altona, shake Virgil manfully by the hand, and stride to the front of the theatre. The audience rises to its feet and applauds with affection and vigour. Obviously, I am a sentimental favourite, and this tribute is either well deserved or long overdue. Or both. I reach the stage, take the Oscar from the presenter (sometimes it's Gene Kelly, sometimes it's Grace Kelly, it doesn't matter that they're dead), and after a decent interval, raise my hands to signal for quiet. The audience takes some time to acquiesce to my wish. Then, in a sure and steady voice, I deliver a brief but emotional address in which I not only acknowledge everyone who needs to be thanked but speak out eloquently and apolitically for world peace and say a few words that are sure to be of comfort to the sick and the dying and downtrodden, then leave the stage, clutching my statue, to another thundering ovation. There have been times when I've been so caught up in this imagining that

Over [Charles] Lamb, at this period of his life, there passed regularly, after taking wine, a brief eclipse of sleep. It descended upon him as softly as a shadow. In a gross person, laden with superfluous flesh, and sleeping heavily, this would have been disagreeable; but in Lamb, thin even to meagreness, spare and wiry as an Arab of the desert, or as Thomas Aquinas, wasted by scholastic vigils, the affection of sleep seemed rather a network of aerial gossamer than of earthly cobweb—more like a golden haze falling upon him gently from the heavens than a cloud exhaling upwards from the flesh. Motionless in his chair as a bust, breathing so gently as scarcely to seem certainly alive, he presented the image

the water has cooled around me in the tub.

My other fantasy, which I have been weaving since childhood, has to do with the way in which I would act during an impromptu meeting with royalty. In recent years, I have adapted this daydream to our present home and circumstances. Here's what happens. The queen and the prince turn up at the door of our B&B. Sometimes they need directions. Sometimes they need to use the loo. Always, I comport myself with detachment, with sang-froid. I'm polite but not fawning, suggesting by my every response and action that this is an everyday occurrence. Showing neither surprise nor discomfiture, I ask them in. They visit the facilities or study a map as the case may be, and then ask if I would show them the house. I do.

"What a charming inn!" they exclaim. "Might we stay the night?"

I shake my head, gravely, for we are completely booked. If only they had made a reservation!

"Ah," they say. "Next time, we'll know better."

And off they go, disappointed, but nonetheless grateful.

I have played out this scenario time and time again in my head and at no time have I ever curtsied. And yet, curtsy is what I did when I went bleary-eyed and tousled to the door and found myself looking down into the sharp and blinking eyes of the queen.

"Good afternoon," she said, as I dipped my knees. They cracked ominously. There was no mistaking the voice: somewhat pinched, a little nose-centred, crisply English, supremely confident. She was smaller than I had imagined and looked older than she does on our stamps. She was dressed for a country walk: sensible shoes, a green plaid skirt, and a plain cloth coat of indubitable pedigree. The only thing overtly regal about her was the diamond-encrusted tiara that glimmered under her head scarf. She carried the ubiquitous handbag, an alligator purse.

"Good afternoon," I answered, "your uh . . . uh . . . your . . . "

I was seized in the moment by a meddlesome indecisiveness. Was it "Your Majesty" or "Your Highness?" Or was there some other honorific for such an occasion?

"Lost?" she asked, supplying the word for which she evidently believed I was fumbling. "No, not lost, exactly. But we are missing something. May we come in?"

"Of course!"

I stepped aside to let her pass and looked into the yard to see if there were any traces of footmen, or corgis, or horses, or gold leaf, or paparazzi, or any of the other hangers-on one might reasonably expect when the monarch comes through. There were none.

"We hope we're not disturbing you?" she asked as she peeled off her gloves.

"Oh, no! We—that is, I—was just having a little nap, and—"

"Did we interrupt your nap? Oh, dear! We're so sorry! We hate it when that happens to us."

"It's really of no importance. May I offer you a cup of tea?"

By this time I was beginning to find my queen legs and was ready to hatch the royal visit game plan on which I had roosted for so long.

"Tea? No thanks. Never touch the stuff. However, we wonder if you might be able to help us out."

"If it's a room you're requiring, I'm afraid . . . "

"Room? No, no. We're on a scavenger hunt, and we've managed to snag everything on our list except for one thing."

"Scavenger hunt?"

of repose of sculpture; and, to one who knew his history, a repose affectingly contrasting with the calamities and internal storms of his life.
—Thomas De Quincey, *Leaders in Literature*

The queen gave an exasperated little sigh.

"Oh yes, surely you know. It's a party game. Tiresome really. One gets a list of oddities and then one must go out into the world and gather them up. We wish we hadn't agreed to play, but one must finish what one starts."

She reached into her alligator handbag and pulled out a well-folded piece of paper.

"Our list. Now, most of this stuff was a cinch," she said, extracting her glasses from the depths of her purse. She put them on and squinted at her catalogue of required goodies.

"Oh, dear! This won't do! These are our tatting glasses."

She threw them aside, reached into the purse, and withdrew another pair.

"Oh, dear! We wear these for driving!"

She continued to rummage about.

"And these are our cheese-grating specs. And these? Damn! These are for counting swans. Where are those bloody reading glasses? We can't make out a word without them. Look, would you mind helping us out?"

She handed me the well-creased page.

"Just read this aloud, and we'll check to see that everything we require is there."

"One bottle of chilled champagne," I read, and after some rummaging, she pulled one from her purse and set it down on the table.

"Ha! Knew it was there somewhere!"

"A Ouija board," I continued, and once again she yanked the listed item from the alligator purse. "A willow ware cup with a broken handle. A walking stick. A basketball hoop. A slice of angel food cake. A salt shaker shaped like a poodle. A satin pillow from Niagara Falls. A snow dome with a Mountie on a horse. A caboose from a model train set. A fez."

One by one I rhymed off the treasures. One by one she reeled them from her seemingly bottomless purse and added them to the growing pile.

"A gargoyle."

"*Voilà*!" she exclaimed. It had a familiar look to it.

"Do you mind my asking where you got that?"

"Old fellow down the road."

"I wondered if that might not be the case."

"Seemed happy to get rid of it. Can't say we blame him, looks just like one of our daughters-in-law. And look! Our reading glasses! We knew they were here somewhere."

I returned to the list.

"There's only one item left. A Polaroid snapshot of a man in the bath."

"That's it! That's what we're missing!"

"Ah."

A silence settled on the room.

"I don't suppose you have such a thing, do you?"

"What? A Polaroid of a man sitting in the bath? No. I'm sorry, I'd have to disappoint you."

"Well, you must have a bathtub."

"Oh, yes. Several, in fact."

"Excellent! And you are a man."

"Certainly. But I—"

"Then we're set! We're sure we have a camera with us, somewhere. Nothing in the rules to say we can't take the damn thing ourselves. Anyway, the end justifies the means. And *honi soit qui mal y pense*, we always say."

There was a tremendous clanking as she rooted through the bag. The camera emerged into the light, its strap wrapped around a crowbar.

"Perfect! Now we're set! Where's the tub?"

And without waiting for a reply, she scuttled upstairs, with me following in her wake.

When Virgil came home later that same afternoon, he found me in the kitchen. I was slicing onions.

"What's new?"

"Not so very much," I answered. I had spent the last hour steeping myself in nonchalance, rehearsing how I would tell my marvellous tale. "Nothing at all, really. Oh! I nearly forgot. We did have one visitor while you were out."

"Who was that?" he asked, opening the fridge and peering into its well-lit, icy heart.

"It's funny you should ask. I'd stretched out on the couch, thinking I might catch forty winks when—"

Just then we heard the crunch of tires on our driveway gravel, and the peremptory hooting of a horn. I looked out the window and saw Altona stepping from her car. She was flushed and grinning from lobe to lobe as she bounced through the kitchen door

Virgil said, "You're looking pleased with yourself. What's up?"

"You're just in time to hear my story," I said. "I was explaining to Virgil . . . "

But Altona was in a talking rather than in a listening kind of mood.

"By golly, but there are days when I love my job! You'll never guess what story I've been covering this afternoon!

Virgil arched an eyebrow.

Your Love Life in the Stars
by Altona Winkler

SCORPIO
October 24 to November 22

Oh, Scorpio, you are bad! I know what you're thinking, and you should stop it right now! For one thing, that butcher is married. He just takes off his ring so as not to catch his finger in the grinder. And you're not the

“Has one of those bevies of Australian male strippers come to the island?”

“Even better! The I.S.Q.I. is having their conference in Victoria, and they came over on a day trip.”

“The I.S.Q.I.?”

“The International Society of Queen Impersonators, of course! They decided to get out of town for a scavenger hunt. I’ll tell you, a more fun-loving group of fellas you could never hope to meet. I was just down taking a group picture at the ferry dock. Imagine! Twenty-five guys, and each and every one of them dudded up like Her Maj! You have never seen such a collection of handbags, floral hats and sensible shoes. Fabulous! I’d love to see them on a formal evening!”

“What on earth would International Queen Impersonators look for on a scavenger hunt?”

“It looked like the usual stuff. A fountain pen, a Shakespeare play, a ginger grater. Oh, and one of them had a Polaroid that was causing quite a stir.”

“Polaroid?” I asked. My throat tightened like a noose around the last syllable. My voice shot up an octave, and Virgil lobbed me a quizzical glance. I coughed in an effort to hide my alarm and effected a quick recovery. “A Polaroid, you say! How novel. I don’t suppose you actually saw the picture?”

“No, but I think it might have been of a stein of beer. There was a lot of giggling about what fun it would be to blow away the suds.”

“Ah ha. Ah ha ha ha,” I laughed, rather weakly.

“Toodle-oo, then! I’d better nip off and have my own film processed!”

She leaned over and gave me a kiss on the cheek.

only one on whom he looks with deep and meaningful eyes, all the while whispering passionately of lean cuts and trimmed fat and butterflied legs of this or that. You’re wasting your time on him. However, check out the hunk in the produce department! Ask him to show you how to look for ripe melons or something. Bark up the right tree, Scorpio, and happiness will be yours.

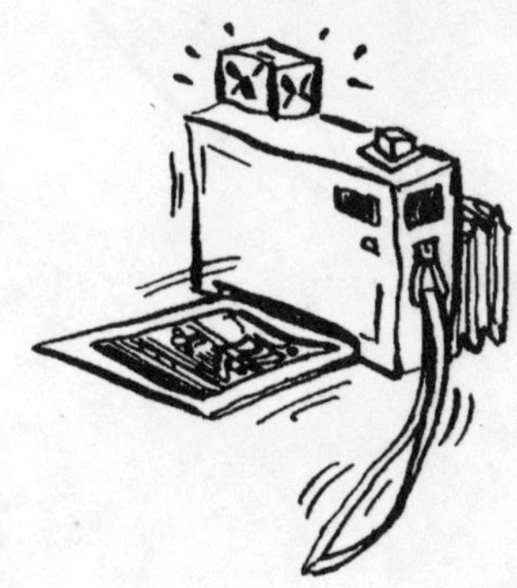

"Mmmmmm! You smell like lilac! You must have been using that bubble bath I gave you!"

And Altona was gone.

"It's good to see someone enjoying her work," said Virgil, waving good-bye as she drove out of the driveway. "And you're certainly lucky to have someone to keep you supplied with bubble bath. There's nothing like a nice *sudsy* soak to restore the spirits."

I didn't like the emphasis he laid on "sudsy."

"Now, what were you about to say? Something about someone dropping by?"

"Oh, yes. Well, it was no one really. Just a Fuller brush salesman."

"Tsk. What a nuisance. Did he give you the old hard sell? Did he talk you into buying something?"

"Oh, no. I was firm. I just sent him on his way."

"Good. Although it's too bad you didn't ask him if he had a high-powered bathtub cleanser. The one liability of that lilac bubble bath is that it stains the tub. Why, in just a couple of days it can verge on royal purple! Perhaps I'll see if I can scrub it away before dinner. After all, you can never tell who might drop by unannounced."

"No. No, you never can."

I will hand it to him. He never once smirked or let on that he knew. Which of course he did. And what's more, he knew that I knew that he knew. But Virgil is the very model of self-control and discretion. He was halfway up the stairs before he even so much as chuckled. I returned to my onions. By rights, I ought to have felt foolish. But somehow, I found it all rather grand and tragic. A tale of generosity and deceit! In an instant, I saw that it would work so well on the big screen! In an instant, I was thanking the Academy for my award.

Virgil: Missing in Action

Back in the olden days, when we were young, before on-line electronic records became the norm, before you could look up any book in the world on a laptop computer, library catalogues were hulking great cabinets jammed with neatly typed 3" x 5" cards that described and situated a book's author, title, and subject. Those cards were artful things. Careful and assiduous scribes, following a series of rules as stringent and demanding as those that govern the writing of a sestina, typed out the pertinent bibliographical details and filed the cards in their alphabetical ranks. Among the essential bits of information noted thereon were the author's birth and death dates. Should the individual have been living at the time the card was created, the birth year was duly noted, followed by a dash and a space to indicate that the business of breathing was still underway. For instance, if a library acquired *Portrait of the Artist as a Young Dog* in 1943, the catalogue card would have been inscribed: Thomas, Dylan, 1914– . After his alcohol-induced death ten years later, the cataloguer went dutifully through with a pen and filled in the anticipatory blank with 1953 on each and every card. I always found those addenda particularly poignant.

There is another writer, also born in 1914, who isn't half as famous as Dylan Thomas, but whose entry in the library catalogue is just as tender, and at least twice as tantalizing. It must have afforded the cataloguers of yore a great deal of macabre pleasure to thumb through the cards and close off his entries in this unusual way: *Kees, Weldon, 1914–1955 ?*. It's that question mark that really makes you sit up and take note; for how often is

The End of the Library

by Weldon Kees

When the coal
Gave out, we began
Burning the books, one by one:
First the set
Of Bulwer-Lytton
And then the Walter Scott.
They gave a lot of warmth.
Toward the end, in
February, flames
Consumed the Greek
Tragedians and Baudelaire,
Proust, Robert Burton
And the Po-Chu-i. Ice
Thickened on the sills.
More for the sake of the cat,
We said, than for ourselves,
Who huddled, shivering,
Against the stove
All winter long.

the year of a death, especially in the twentieth century, in any way equivocal? Why does Weldon rate such a rarity?

Kees was an astonishing character. As a poet, he is relatively little read: in part because not many people read poetry, in part because his output was small, and, in part, because what remains—and his collected verse can be found in one quite small volume—is bleak. It's suffused with a kind of post-Hiroshima mordancy, and the word "uplifting" doesn't leap to the forefront of the mind.

Cheerless though his verses be, I have a soft spot in my heart for Weldon Kees. I found him at the tag end of my adolescence when Anne Sexton and Sylvia Plath and Hart Crane and other poets of the self-destructive school had become my required reading. Through their despondency, I was able to siphon off puberty's more nihilistic tendencies. I was perversely fascinated by writers whose lives had a tragic cast to them, and the Kees biography was uncommonly invigorating. He was not only a poet. He wrote plays and criticism and published over forty short stories. He was the co-author and the photographer of a ground-breaking book called *Notes on the Visual Perception of Human Relations*. He was a painter who mounted shows in New York with abstract expressionists like Hofmann and de Kooning. He was an accomplished jazz pianist and composer. He was active as a filmmaker.

And in 1955, Weldon Kees vanished without trace. His car was found near the Golden Gate Bridge. Most people drew the sad and logical conclusion. He had been behaving oddly, had been even more despondent than usual, had spoken with his friends about ending it all. The body was never recovered. Perhaps it was sucked out to sea by the tides. But some of Kees's acquaintances recalled how he'd batted around the notion that he would go to Mexico and shed his tragic skin; that he would start afresh with a new name, a different identity. True enough, it has the sound of a desperate man's dumb and quixotic plan. But in the absence of concrete evidence to utterly disprove it, it's a possibility that has to be taken into account. Witness the telltale "?" in the library catalogue: a decades-old testament to a small mystery, and to the grim and happy hours one might have concocting possibilities that are less run-of-the-mill than simple slippage. Perhaps he came north. Perhaps he's with us still. Weldon! Weldon! If you're within the sound of my voice—call home. There's something I'm dying to ask you.

Getting to Sleep: A Victorian Recipe

The Victorian almanac *Enquire Within Upon Everything* is a tubby trove of charming and eccentric counsel that we always keep to hand. Here is some useful advice from it:

How to get to sleep is to many persons a matter of high importance. Nervous persons who are troubled with wakefulness and excitability usually have a strong tendency of blood on the brain, with cold extremities. The pressure of the blood on the brain keeps it in a stimulated or wakeful state, and the pulsations in the head are often painful. Let such rise and chafe the body and extremities with a brush or towel, or run smartly with the hands to promote circulation and withdraw the excessive amount of blood from the brain, and they will fall asleep in a few moments. A cold bath, or a sponge bath and rubbing, or a good run, or a rapid walk in the open air, or going up or down stairs a few times

before retiring, will aid in equalising circulation and promoting sleep. These rules are simple and easy of application in castle or cabin and may minister to the comfort of thousands who would freely expend money for an anodyne to promote "Nature's sweet restorer, balmy sleep!"

From *Personal Pleasures* *by Rose Macaulay*

Climb, then, into this paradise, this epicurism of pleasure, this pretty world of peace. Push up the pillows, that they support the head at an angle as you lie sideways, your book held in one hand, its edge resting on the pillow. On the bed-head is a bright light canopied by an orange shade; it illustrates the page with soft radiance, so that it shines out of the environing shadows like a good deed in a naughty world. You are reading, I would suggest, a novel; preferably a novel which excites you by its story, lightly titillating, but not furrowing, the surface of the brain. Not poetry; not history; not essays; not voyages; not biography, archaeology, dictionaries, nor that peculiar literature which publishers call belles-lettres. These are for day-time reading; they are not somnifacient; they stimulate the mind, the aesthetic and appreciative faculties, the inventive imagination; in brief, they wake you up. You will never, I maintain, get to sleep on Shakespeare, Milton, or Marvell, or Hakluyt, or Boswell, or Montaigne, or Burton's *Anatomy*, or Sir Thomas Browne, or Herodotus, or any poetry or prose that fundamentally excites you by its beauty, or any work that imparts knowledge. These will light a hundred candles in your brain, startling it to vivid life. A story, and more particularly a story you have not read before, will hold your attention gently on the page, leading it on from event to event, drowsily pleased to be involved in such fine adventures, which yet demand no thought. Let the story amuse, thrill, interest, delight, it matters not which; but let it not animate, stimulate or disturb, for sleep, the shy nightbird, must not be startled back as it hovers over you with drowsy wings, circling ever near and nearer, until its feathers brush your eyes and the book dips suddenly in your hand. Lay it aside then; push out the light; the dark bed, like a gentle pool of water, receives you; you sink into its encompassing arms, floating down the wandering trail of a dream, as down some straying river that softly twists and slides through goblin lands, now dipping darkly into blind caves, now emerging, lit with the odd, phosphorescent light on oneiric reason, unsearchable and dark to waking eyes.

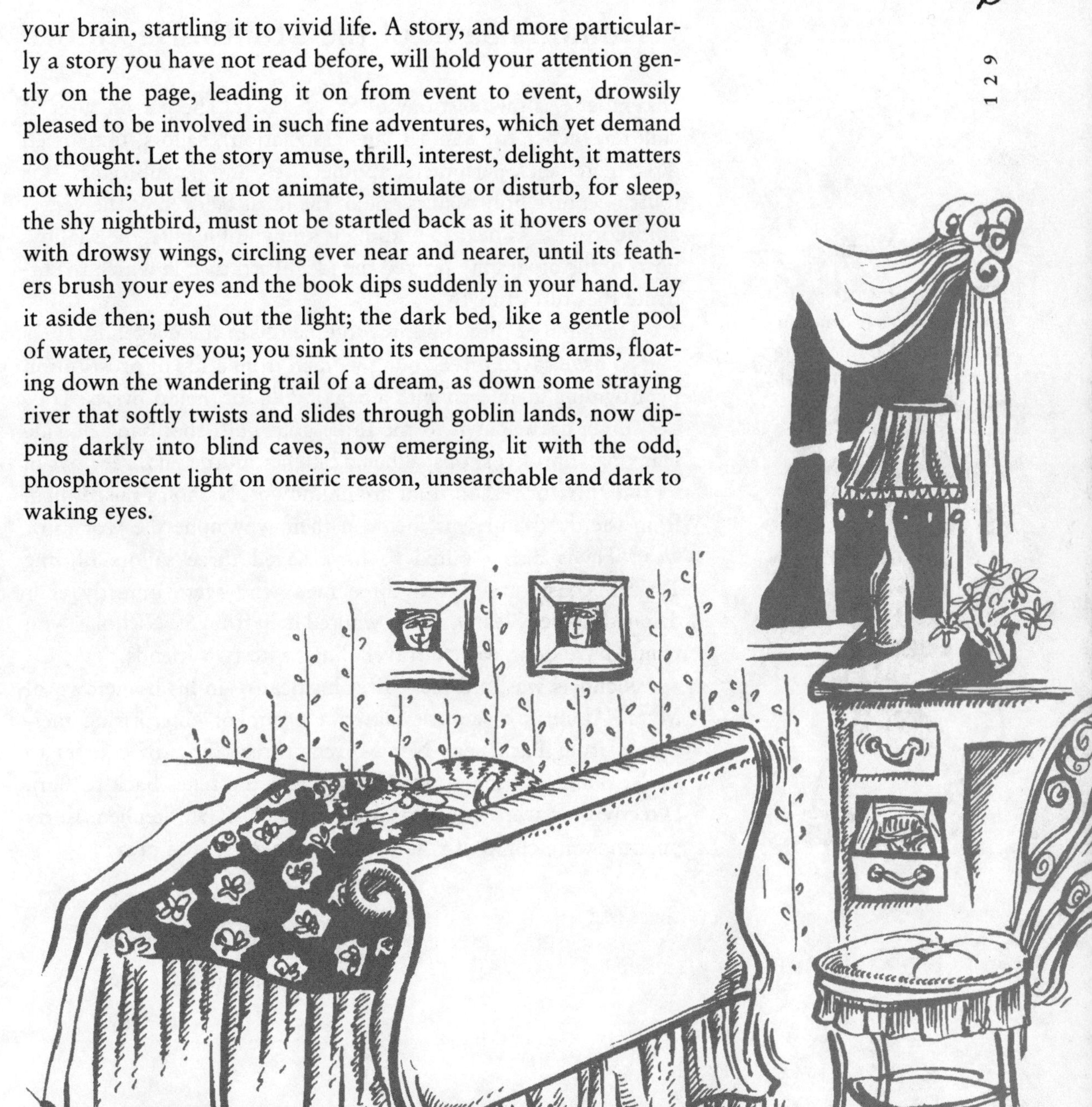

Caedmon's Saint of the Month: December

December 6 is the feast day of St. Nicholas. The patron saint of children (hence the Santa Claus association), sailors, unmarried girls, merchants, perfumers, apothecaries, and pawnbrokers, this fourth-century holy man is one of the most beloved of the venerable worthies. As next to nothing is known of his life, the shallow bowl of his biography proved the ideal Petri dish in which to cultivate the stuff of myth.

The number three figures prominently in these legends. He is said to have saved three young women from a life of prostitution by providing them each with a bag of gold for their dowries. This, say some, gave spawn to the three gold balls that hang outside many pawnbroker shops. When a butcher murdered three boys in a brine tub (for reasons that are unknown), Nicholas raised them from the dead and sent them on their way none the worse for wear. He is also reputed to have saved three sailors off the Turkish coast, and saved three men who were unjustly condemned to die. Clearly, if you wanted help from St. Nicholas, you would have done well to travel about with two friends.

Nicholas was interred—after his death—in his hometown of Myra. About six centuries later, a group of enterprising merchants from Bari, near Naples, sent three ships (of course) to Lycia, plundered the grave, and brought the relics back to Bari. Directly they were installed in the Church of St. Stephen, thirty pilgrims were cured of whatever ailed them. Let us pray:

To Cure Warts

To get rid of warts, you must wash your hands in the rays of a full moon in a dry and empty metal dish, while saying:

I wash my hands
in this thy dish,
Oh man in the moon,
do grant my wish,
And come and take
away this.

Yuletide comes, the bills mount up, the stores sell off their stock,
Let us pray St. Nicholas will keep us out of hock.
As he plucked the butchered boys from out the salty brine,
May he always help us tow the sacred credit line;
Otherwise we'll be compelled to leave the tinselled halls
And swap our Christmas loot for cash beneath three hanging balls.

Our Guests Write: Trudy

Dear Hector and Virgil:

Best of the season. I want you both to know that you hold in your hands the evidence that it is possible to keep a New Year's resolution. Last year I vowed that I would not allow myself to be beaten, yet again, by Christmas. And as you can see, I have sent out the cards (which, I'll have you know, I purchased on sale last Boxing Day) a full three weeks in advance of the day. Will wonders never cease? And it gets better! Not only am I ahead of the game on the card front, I have also started my baking. And furthermore, I have gone so far as to disinter the decorations from their attic resting place. What happy domestic archaeology that is, finding the crackers that didn't get pulled last year, the choirboy I made in the fifth grade (from a magazine, a dowel stick, and a styrofoam ball), the tree danglers, the lights, the tinsel, and the glass balls wrapped in last January's newspaper. And sometimes, there are surprises.

I paused in my rummaging to open a box that wasn't marked but looked very much as if it might contain a gay garland or two.

To Cure a Burn

Three ladies
came from the East
One with fire
and two with frost.
Out with thee fire
and in with thee frost.

In fact, its tenants were some English Lit. papers I had written when I was at university, fully two decades ago. I have completely lost track of the impulse that made me set them aside when so much else has been wilfully discarded. It doesn't much matter. The point is that I stopped what I was doing and plunked myself down to read.

There was an essay dated January 3, 1974, called (believe it or not) "Wanderers of the Dark: Insanity in King Lear." On April 7, 1975, I submitted an odious tract entitled "Fighting Gravity: A Study of Suffering in the Oedipus Plays and Job." And more loathsome still was a paper that fairly staggered under the weight of its title: "The Multidirectional, Multidimensional Implications of the Plumtree's Potted Meat Motif in James Joyce's *Ulysses.*"

The horror! The horror! I read these deliberations, and I blushed reindeer-nose red. Did I actually write the portentous, pretentious sentence, "As Lear's anger rises and insanity looms ever closer, a definite change in his mentality is manifesting itself"? Yikes! That's enough to make anyone gouge out his eyes. Or how about, "In this essay, I plan to examine how Oedipus and Job react to the existential dilemma of their suffering and how ultimately they come to fulfil the role of heroic prototype." Ooooo! Guess who'd just discovered Joseph Campbell! Worse still, "My final illustration of the sexual dimension of the many-faceted Plumtree's Potted Meat motif revolves around the frequently discussed and highly coveted Ascot Gold Cup, a prestigious award offered as the prize in a horse race being run that day." Excuse me? What the hell does that mean? And besides, what would I know about sexual dimensions? I don't think I'd even had sex at that point in my life!

Oh, my dears! It was more horrible than I can tell you. Such

Your Love Life in the Stars
by Altona Winkler

SAGITTARIUS
November 23 to December 21

Try to work against your tendency to be standoffish. Give serious consideration to a mid-month invitation to a Twister party. If such an invitation doesn't materialize, you might consider having a Twister party yourself! It's a great way to mix and mingle. If you're over forty, be sure to include a chiropractor on your guest list.

pomposity and self-importance! Such vacuity and dishonesty! Such bad, bad writing! I punctuated my reading of these essays with gasps of embarrassment and awful recognition. It was like looking at candid photos taken at a drunken party. Omigod! Was that really me at eighteen, imparting to my forty-year-old self the news that "King Lear is a play rife with the starkest of mental anguish"? Did I really have the nerve to report that "Those who ride the crest of a popular wave are frequently swept by sudden twists of events into a sea of despair"? Yup. I'm afraid so. It's a good thing I hadn't yet made the shortbread and had no cookies to toss.

With no ceremony whatsoever, I shoved these terrible artifacts back into the unmarked box, pushed it to a corner of the attic, collected up the tinsel, the shiny Santas, and the fragile glass balls, and went downstairs, trailing not clouds of glory but a silver and red garland, and the certainty that the past, when it sneaks up on you, can delight you with its spirit or appall you with its evidence, and that part of the delicious tension of living in the present is never knowing for a certainty when one or the other might happen. Happy, happy Christmas to the both of you! Hope to see you soon in the New Year.
Trudy Allbright, Spokane, Washington

Reading What the Wind Brought: A Newspaper Clipping

Not so very long ago, I was browsing, idly, in a neighbourhood antique store. Artfully displayed amidst the inlaid nesting tables and the cut-glass pickle dishes and the watch fobs and the sad, shiny remnants of someone's family silver, was a tiger-skin rug. I was fascinated, as I'd never seen such a thing before. It called up all manner of picturesque, airless roomscapes: Victorian parlours and dark-panelled rooms illumined by sunbeams thick with dust motes falling on a clutter of doilies and antimacassars. Beadwork lampshades and sandalwood boxes and a tabby cat stretched supine on the skin of his near and distant relative: a tiger who never once, in her darkest jungle dreams, imagined she would end up in a place like this.

Of course, I reached out to touch it, to stroke it, to pet it, as I would never have dared had the original owner been attached. You should know that I am not psychically adept. Still, I could almost feel, coursing up through the coarse filaments of the pelt, a hot lusting after life, a current of unalloyed sensuality, an easy acquaintance with the smell and taste of blood, a pride and confidence and uncluttered sense of place and purpose. This was the striped, stylish coat of someone who had lived for her work, and that work had been nothing more than the simple business of being herself in the narrow confines of her world. And now, here she was. Had I been willing to shell out 3500 bucks, I could have had all that was left of her.

That tiger came to mind when I heard a radio news report out of India. It had to do with the tigers, and how the most optimistic conservationists think the great cats have maybe five years left before the last of them falls. And this dwindling has not even occurred in the name of something as tangible as a carseat cover. No, the tigers have been done in so their bones can be made into medicines and wines which are meant to ensure the continued potency of the species that is bent on their decimation. Consider the irony.

I know very well that every day the Catalogue of Extinction grows thicker with the added names of plants, bugs, birds. I know that, and yet I manage to accommodate the information with a little *moue* of distress, a tsk-tsk of studied alarm. I have no reason to suspect that the gloomy prospects for the tiger—gone for good before the century gasps its last—are, in the grand scheme of things, any more significant than the loss of, say, some dun-bellied dumbledore from the Carpathian Mountains. Whole earth thinking teaches us that one species is as valuable and pivotal to the health of Gaia as any other. And if the tiger goes, what do we really lose? A conspicuous name. A pretty rug. A source of tonics. So what? If that's what we really want—and evidently, it is—there'll still be a few bears or bighorn sheep to take up the slack. And by the time they've been used up, we'll probably be able to remake them in the laboratory. So, what's the point in fretting about the tiger, especially since it sounds as though the deal's already done?

When the last tiger gets snuffed, the jungle will know and mourn in its own green way. I suppose it will take months before there's a press release telling the rest of us. Even before the fact is revealed, we will all of us have been dealt a powerful blow to the imagination. What we will lose, then and irrevocably, is an image, which is even more powerful than tooth and claw. We will lose

the possibility of the word becoming flesh: the delicious nightmare that somewhere, out in the tall grass, waits a powerful embodiment of otherness that would happily remove our throats in a single, guiltless swipe. We lose a being to whom we can impute the salutary quality of inspiring terror. Very soon there will be nothing and no one left on earth capable of hefting around that awful burden except us. And when that happens—in five more years—we will richly, richly deserve the burden of it.

Aunt Jennifer's Tigers
by Adrienne Rich

Aunt Jennifer's tigers prance across a screen,
Bright topaz denizens of a world of green.
They do not fear the men beneath the tree;
They pace in sleek chivalric certainty.

Aunt Jennifer's fingers fluttering through her wool
Find even the ivory needle hard to pull.
The massive weight of Uncle's wedding band
Sits heavily upon Aunt Jennifer's hand.

When Aunt is dead, her terrified hands will lie
Still ringed with ordeals she was mastered by.
The tigers in the panel that she made
Will go on prancing, proud and unafraid.

What to Expect when the Rapture Comes

And on the final day, when the last trump had sounded; when the just and the dead rose incorruptible from even the deepest of their tombs, joyful and triumphant, minty breathed and eager to meet their maker face to face; when the hollow-eyed, impartial horsemen of the Apocalypse galloped along the globe's every meridian, brandishing their shining scythes and collecting the wages of sin; when all the clouds choreographed themselves into a synchronized display so that the numbers 666 dangled visible for all to see between the firmament and the cracking crust of the earth; when the head of every pin was dense with dancing angels, when pigs grew wings and when lions lay down with lambs; when the furious face of our fulminating Father, big as all Pittsburgh, loomed into view from beyond the remotest of galaxies, his mouth open and ready to swallow the sun like a half-sucked lozenge: then it was that every insubstantial thought balloon, hanging in the once-recumbent air over each and every cat—whether tabby, calico, Manx, or Persian, whether balanced on a fencepost or languishing on a lap—demonstrated its intense frangibility and ruptured.

Yea, verily, it was a day of wonders! And chief among them was when cat words spilled forth into the air. This was revelation. From generation unto generation, from the beginning till the end of time, the cats, silent and purposeful, had kept their kitty counsel. Dainty yogis with their hind legs poised in impossible extensions or with their paws curled up beneath their chests, testing their own heartbeats, they observed the world and its querulous ways through the slits of their hooded, patrician eyes, chanting their timeless mantras, rolling over and over on their tongues the occult hymns of praise and thanksgiving that are as intrinsic to their beings as whiskers and purring.

"What are they thinking?" dull-witted humans have wondered, ever since the first cat sat by the first fire and let it be known that here she was at home and would not willingly go hence. But it was not until the last day was fully upon us, when all things hidden were fully revealed, that their arcane thoughts and hitherto inscrutable meditations were made audible, and the voices of cats took their place in the massed choir whose singing accompanied the final gasping moments of life on earth. Here, then, is one small snippet of that revealed word, one psalm out of the many that were heard on that great getting up morning when we gathered at the river and the sweet chariot swung low.

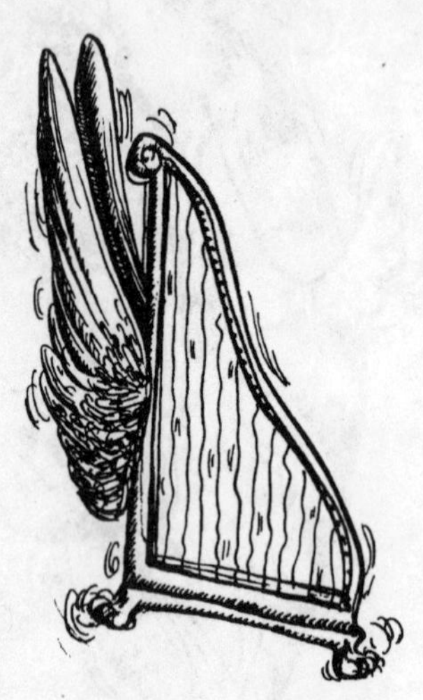

Cat Psalm 17

1. Hear me, oh great one, when I cry to thee in thy dwelling place! Hear me, for I speak with the voice of the just! Hear me, for I am righteous, and I walk the good walk. And my name shall be Blameless.

2. Blameless shall they call me, and I walk the good walk the whole length of a mantelpiece laden with the most garish ornaments: chachkas for which breakage would be too kind a fate, lava lamps, and worse. Agile shall they call me, and I shall negotiate my way through such brute nastiness as this, and there shall be no smashing.

3. And smashing shall I reserve for a single and very expensive Baccarat vase that sits by itself in the middle of a large and uncluttered table and that only an act of malicious will could destroy. And I shall look innocent, and Blameless shall be my name.

4. And your couches will be mine for the shredding, and your divans shall I leave in tatters, and you shall buy your costly scratching posts in vain.

5. Put up your doors, oh upright walkers! For you shall not keep me out, and you shall not keep me in. I shall show you how little I care for your gates. For I shall cause you to open them with nothing more than a long and forthright look. And I shall cause you to close them with a prolonged and shuddering miaow. And a period of no more than thirty seconds shall elapse between the opening and the closing, and entrance and egress shall be as one.

6. And your ankles were made for no other purpose than for me to make a demonstration of my able and sinewy winding. For your laps are a slate on which I can perfect my kneading.

7. Make mine tuna.

8. Suffer me not to be belled, oh great one! For starlings are plentiful and stupid, and death at my paw is really too good for them, but we all have to go sometime, and if it be thy will that I should be the agent of their demise, then so be it, and who am I to argue?

9. Deliver me from liver.

10. For mine is the kingdom, forever and ever, and I shall always walk the good walk. The good walk shall always be mine and I shall be Blameless. Thus saith the cat, and the cat saith right. Amen.

The Cat's Christmas Vigil

The cat was the last one left awake that night. She sat on the window ledge, looking out. It was dark, and it was empty; but as vistas go, it was a damn sight more interesting than the room on which she had turned her sleek black back. "They who open tins," as she contemptuously called the tall and clumsy ones, were gape-jawed in their beds, expelling fetid wind with each snore and dreaming fretfully of the lamb vindaloo they'd intemperately eaten mere hours before. The dog—who as far as she was concerned took up far too much space on the planet and had proved herself time and again to be useless as an accomplice—twitched in her basket, cooking up self-important dreams of squirrels and robbers. God! How tedious! Why did she stay, anyway? Her colleagues were somnolent and incompetent. The grub was barely tolerable. No one would call the accommodations deluxe. There was no remuneration and too much grief by half. It was more than she could bear.

She shifted on her elegant haunches, settling into the grudging certainty that if it was amusement she was after, she would have to rely on her inner resources rather than on outside stimulation. She dealt her paw a disconsolate lick, wedging her tongue between her taloned toes with considerable panache and agility.

She was savouring the flavour of her foot's deepest crevice when she heard the bells. She sat up straight and tilted her silk purse ears towards the sound. Silence. Then the ringing again: three distinct bells, small, rich, and clear, walloping through the night. She peered out, narrowing her burnished eyes, separating their folds one by one. She took it all in: the building across the street, the shabby corner grocery, the naked chestnut tree with its empty birdnests, the sign with its ironic inscription: "CAUTION: LIMITED VISION."

Then, the first camel hove into view. Then another. Then a third. Three camels with three riders and three camel bells ringing ambled down the street outside her house and came to a stop right beneath her window. Well, then! This was something new! She thought for a moment or two about waking the tall ones so that they might have a look, but decided against it. Some treats were just too delicious to share.

The camels were tall and handsome beasts with nostrils the size of small planets, chorus-line legs, and a nice line of saddle blankets. They moved their jaws in a ruminative way that made them appear to be either chewing gum or tobacco or grazing the sky. They stood with an air of patient forbearance the cat understood only too well. The men who straddled their backs seemed to be suited up for a costume party. Their outfits were outlandish and festive, and belied their mood. They shook their fists and gesticulated wildly, with no evident purpose. The cat had seen this sort of behaviour often enough before; and even though the exact nuances of human speech were a mystery to her, she was canny enough to penetrate the meaning of their exchange. It wasn't pleasant. She knew that each man was trying to convince the other two that *he* was right and *they* were wrong, and that the

Walk fast in snow,
in frost walk slow,
And still as you go
tread on your toe;
When frost and snow
are both together,
Sit by the fire and
spare shoe leather.

mess in which they found themselves in the present moment could have been easily circumvented if *he* had only been allowed to have *his* way. The camels yawned. One of them lobbed a great volley of spit into a hedge, demonstrating an accuracy and aplomb that the cat admired. That was a talent she liked to cultivate, to enliven her idle moments.

One of the riders reached into his saddlebag and pulled out a tattered map. He turned it one way. The second rider turned it another. The third threw his hands in the air and let fly with a volley of curses. Across the street, someone leaned out a window and threw a shoe. All three riders turned and shook their fists. The first crumpled the map and kicked his camel in the ribs. It lurched into action. The other two followed suit. The cat watched them until they disappeared around the corner. A few minutes later, she could no longer hear the bells.

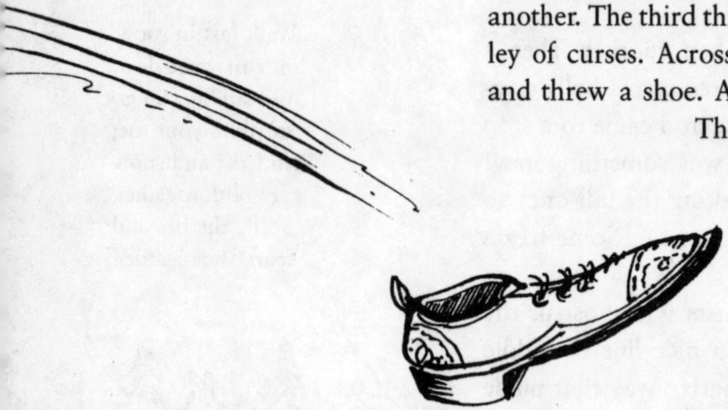

Now, *that* had been worth waiting up for. She left the window and stretched herself across the vulnerable throat of a tall one. Who were the strangers? Where were they going? From where were they coming? What were they seeking? Where did they get their hats? How long had the camels put up with them? Oh, there were stories that begged inventing! But not now. Now, she was tired. These were things she would keep in her heart, storing them there for future pondering.

Virgil: Coda

Waffle loves to use my head as a lounge. It half makes me wonder if in an earlier life she might have been a toupee. She is an agile cat and partial to clambering. She can scale the length of my body, shinnying from base to summit, in under five seconds. To do so, she jumps from the floor to my calf, extends her reach to the buttocks and the middle back, then achieves a wobbly hold on the shoulders before finally planting her flag on the crown of the skull. My body is crossed with cicatrices that tell the gory tale of her exertions.

I have grown so accustomed to the presence of this feline *perruque* that I often forget she's there until I catch sight of her reflected back to me from the kettle or a glass ball on our Christmas tree. Just now, I was placing some socks (hand-knitted, a gift from Altona) in my bureau drawer and saw the two of us framed by the dresser mirror, saw the little calico on my cranium, her legs wrapped around my forehead, her lethal paws looking like an extra pair of eyebrows. I could feel the warm, ever-so-slightly damp spray of her breath on my forehead. It was an odd but peaceful moment. I can't for the life of me understand why mischief chose that moment to take hold of me: a boyish impulse, like wanting to toss a stone to startle a meditating frog from its lily pad. So, I jumped but an inch or two into the air—once, twice, three times—wondering if I could rattle Waffle with her own copycat stare. One, two, three little hops.

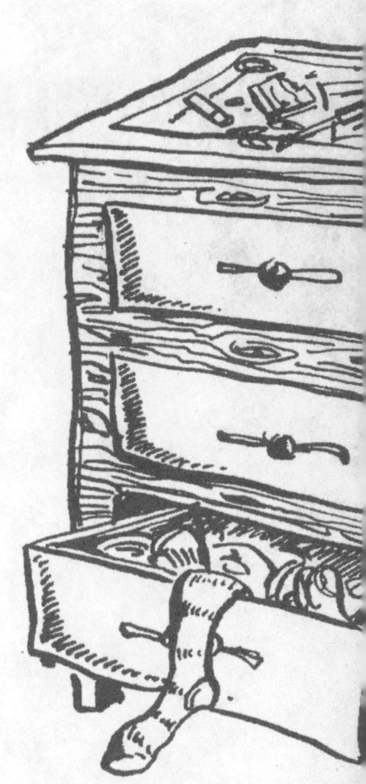

For a moment, there was no response. Then, from some deep place within her, I felt the stir of a purr. She opened her eyes to their demi-slit, half-mast position. Small flashes of yellow, green.

She yawned. She lifted her eyelids slowly, slowly, to reveal the full and fiery magnificence of her unsquinting, unstinting regard. She took in the image of both of us. One man, bald and grinning. One cat, sleepy and sprawling. She blinked, deliberately, firmly—which, I am told by usually reliable sources, is the cat sign for "I love you." Then, she adjusted her grip, yawned again and returned to her slumbers.

Now, it is possible—likely, even—that she aimed that wink at herself and herself alone. It may well be that her putative sign of affection was nothing more than kitty *amour propre*. And it is equally possible that she was having me on, that she was being out and out sarcastic, getting her own back. This much I acknowledge. But as there were no other witnesses and as my only confederate shows no inclination to make her own truth be known, the final word belongs to me. So, I choose to claim that wink as my own. And I choose to understand it as a sign of love. I accept it for what it is worth, and it is worth the whole wide world to me. For what could be greater than love freely given and freely accepted? And why should love be valued the less because it comes from a cat? Take your love where you can find it, my friends. Give it where you can. This much we are each of us owed and owing. This much I wish for all of you. And a very good night. Sleep well.